An Introduction to 8086/88 Assembly La
for Engineers

An Introduction to 8086/88 Assembly Language Programming for Engineers

Noel M. Morris

Principal Lecturer
North Staffordshire Polytechnic

McGRAW-HILL Book Company

London · New York · St Louis · San Francisco · Auckland · Bogotá
Guatemala · Hamburg · Lisbon · Madrid · Mexico · Montreal · New Delhi
Panama · Paris · San Juan · São Paulo · Singapore · Sydney · Tokyo · Toronto

Published by
McGRAW-HILL Book Company (UK) Limited
MAIDENHEAD · BERKSHIRE · ENGLAND

British Library Cataloguing in Publication Data

Morris, Noel M.
    8086/88 assembly language programming for engineers.
    1. Engineering–Data processing
    2. Microcomputers–Programming
    3. Assembling (Electronic computers)
    I. Title
    005.2′6   TA345

    ISBN 0-07-084173-X

Library of Congress Cataloging-in-Publication Data

Morris, Noel Malcolm.
    8086/88 assembly language programming for engineers.
    Bibliography: p.
    Includes index.
    1. Intel 8086 (Microprocessor)–Programming.
2. Intel 8088 (Microprocessor)–Programming. 3. Assembler language (Computer program
language) I. Title.
QA76.8.I292M667   1987   005.265   87-14004
ISBN 0-07-085173-X

Printed and bound in Great Britain by the Alden Press, Oxford

Contents

Preface

This book introduces you to assembly language programming using what is arguably the most popular range of 16-bit microprocessors. The treatment is detailed, and is strongly supported by many practical examples of programs which can be run by 8086- and 8088-based microcomputers, such as the IBM microcomputer.

The 8086 is a central processor unit (CPU) which has a 16-bit architecture and a 16-bit external data bus system. The 8088 has the same chip architecture as the 8086, but has an external 8-bit data bus system. It is perhaps the latter feature which has made the 8088 one of the leading CPUs today, and this book is biased towards the use of this chip. Both CPUs have an identical instruction set and, for this reason, the assembly language programs are compatible with one another. Another advantage is that the instruction set of the 8080 and the 8085 are subsets of the instruction set of the 8086 and 8088.

The book provides an introduction to the 8088, and is suitable for a wide range of courses including HNC, HND, degree and postgraduate courses. It will be suitable for the computer novice and the professional alike, and provides an insight into the use of the 8086/88 assembly language. The book has a strong tutorial content, and covers assembly language programming principles and practice, including applications incorporating input/output ports.

Chapter 1 brings the reader to a basic level of knowledge of arithmetic methods used in microcompouters, and introduces important features of the 8086/88, such as the flags which are used, and of the technique of memory segmentation.

Chapter 2 describes the architecture of the 8086 and 8088 chips, together with the three-bus system which controls their operation. A knowledge of the contents of this chapter is essential for a full understanding of the instruction set of the CPU.

Chapter 3 introduces the terminology of assembly language programming. Important information on addressing modes, instruction format and the instruction set is given in this chapter.

Practical programming commences in Chapter 4, and deals with a range of arithmetic and logical operations. Many important aspects of programming are covered, including the process of 'single stepping' through a program in order to study the effects of each instruction. Practical mathematical processes such as binary and decimal addition and subtraction are covered, together with 'unpacked' binary (ASCII) addition and subtraction. Multiplication and division instructions are also covered, along with a wide range of logical operations. This chapter introduces a technique used throughout the book, that is an initial program is introduced at an early point in the chapter and, as the chapter proceeds, the program is modified to take account of developments in the chapter. This enables you to quickly amend your programs to take account of any new information which is provided. The programs are presented in a 'recipe' form, so that the reader gradually masters the complexities of the programming language.

Chapter 5 deals with a range of transfer of control instructions (JuMP and LOOP instructions) together with shift and rotate instructions. In Chapter 6, the important topic of the stack is covered, as are subroutines, procedures, and nested procedures.

Input/output ports are introduced in Chapter 7, and the design of a simple input/output peripheral is described. This peripheral can be connected to one of the I/O chips of the computer and used to simulate many practical systems such as traffic lights, pneumatic and hydraulic systems, etc. The use of the computer as a 'code convertor' is illustrated in this chapter, in which one form of code is 'input' to the CPU via a set of switches, and the converted code is 'output' to a set of lights or light-emitting diodes. This chapter also includes a program which can be used to control a stepper motor of the type used in some robot arms.

Input/output facilities are extended further in Chapter 8, where analogue output and input are covered. In the 'real' world, many signals are analogue in nature, and the programs in this chapter describe methods of dealing with digital-to-analogue conversion (DAC) and analogue-to-digital conversion (ADC). A range of applications is covered, including waveform generation either directly or from data in a table.

8086- and 8088-based microcomputer systems make intensive use of the interrupt facilities of the chip, and these are described in Chapter 9. The chapter includes a practical assembly language program which handles an interrupt produced by a peripheral. The devices connected to the computer, such as the keyboard, the disk(s), and the VDU are interrupt driven and, in Chapter 10, the use of interrupts to transfer text from the memory of the screen is described. Chapter 10 includes a number of programs which deal with string manipulation, together with one which handles the multiplication of unpacked binary-coded decimal numbers.

I would like to thank my colleague, Mr J. S. Zarach, of the Electrical and Electronic Engineering Department of the North Staffordshire Polytechnic for his not inconsiderable help, and the Intel Corporation for permission to publish details of the 8086/88 instruction set. My wife has also provided unflagging support while the book was being written, and it would not have been completed without her assistance.

Whether you are a novice or a professional, you will find something in this book which will aid your understanding of 8086- and 8088-based computing systems at the assembly language level.

Noel M. Morris

1
Bits, bytes, hex, arithmetic and memory segmentation

1.1 The binary system

A *binary numbering system* is a two-level system in which each variable is represented by one of two possible 'levels'; the two levels used are '0' ('zero' or 'false') and '1' ('one' or 'true'). That is, the binary system has a *base* or *radix* of two, corresponding to the number of states that the variable may assume. It is important to remember that the first state is zero, and the second state is 'one'. When dealing with numbering systems, confusion can arise when a number represented by a group of digits, say 111, is being discussed. For example, the question may arise whether the number 111 means decimal one hundred and eleven or whether it means binary 111; the two have vastly different values. To avoid confusion from this cause it is usual, when dealing with non-decimal systems, to include some other information with the number. Either of two methods is adopted; the first is to add a subscript equal to the radix to the number, and the second is to add a letter after the number (usually B for binary). For example,

$$1010 \text{ binary} = 1010_2 = 1010\text{B}$$

In most computer systems, the default radix is decimal, so that if a value is entered into the computer without an alphabetical or other character associated with it, the computer assumes that it is decimal.

Any decimal number can be represented as a binary value by dividing the decimal number into powers of 2 as follows:

$$5 = (1 \times 2^2) + (0 \times 2^1) + (1 \times 2^0) = 101\text{B}$$
$$15 = (1 \times 2^3) + (1 \times 2^2) + (1 \times 2^1) + (1 \times 2^0) = 1111\text{B}$$

Each *binary digit* in the number is referred to as a *bit*.

To convert a decimal number into its binary equivalent, you merely divide the decimal number repeatedly by the radix of the binary system, successive remainders

Table 1.1 Binary and hexadecimal equivalents of the decimal numbers 0–24

Decimal		Binary					Hexadecimal	
10^1	10^0	2^4	2^3	2^2	2^1	2^0	16^1	16^2
0	0	0	0	0	0	0	0	0
0	1	0	0	0	0	1	0	1
0	2	0	0	0	1	0	0	2
0	3	0	0	0	1	1	0	3
0	4	0	0	1	0	0	0	4
0	5	0	0	1	0	1	0	5
0	6	0	0	1	1	0	0	6
0	7	0	0	1	1	1	0	7
0	8	0	1	0	0	0	0	8
0	9	0	1	0	0	1	0	9
1	0	0	1	0	1	0	0	A
1	1	0	1	0	1	1	0	B
1	2	0	1	1	0	0	0	C
1	3	0	1	1	0	1	0	D
1	4	0	1	1	1	0	0	E
1	5	0	1	1	1	1	0	F
1	6	1	0	0	0	0	1	0
1	7	1	0	0	0	1	1	1
1	8	1	0	0	1	0	1	2
1	9	1	0	0	1	1	1	3
2	0	1	0	1	0	0	1	4
2	1	1	0	1	0	1	1	5
2	2	1	0	1	1	0	1	6
2	3	1	0	1	1	1	1	7
2	4	1	1	0	0	0	1	8

giving the binary number (the *least significant bit* [l.s.b.] being given by the first remainder and the *most significant bit* [m.s.b.] being the final remainder). This is illustrated in the following, when the decimal number 23 is converted into pure binary.

$$2\underline{)23}$$

$$2\underline{)11} \quad \text{remainder 1 (l.s.b.)}$$

$$2\underline{)\ 5} \quad \text{remainder 1}$$

$$2\underline{)\ 2} \quad \text{remainder 1}$$

$$2\underline{)\ 1} \quad \text{remainder 0}$$

$$0 \quad \text{remainder 1 (m.s.b.)}$$

$$\text{hence } 23 \ = \ 10111B$$

The pure binary code for decimal numbers from zero to 24 is listed in Table 1.1; as mentioned earlier, the first number is zero, so that 24 is the 25th number in the table.

1.2 The hexadecimal (hex) numbering system

This system has a radix of 16 and is widely used by assembly language programmers. Since it has a radix larger than that of the decimal system, six additional characters have been 'invented' to deal with the decimal values 10 to 15; the alphabetical characters A to F are used in the hexadecimal system as shown in Table 1.1.

Hexadecimal values are indicated either by writing down the radix (16) as a subscript or by writing down the letter 'H' after the hexadecimal number as follows:

$$\text{hexadecimal } 9AF = 9AF_{16} = 9AFH$$

In microcomputing circles, the use of the letter H is common.

A binary number can be converted into its hex equivalent simply by writing down the binary number in groups of four bits (commencing with the l.s.b., the most significant group being completed by adding non-significant zeros), and replacing each group by its hex equivalent as follows:

$$1011101101B = 0010 \quad 1110 \quad 1101B = 2EDH$$

1.3 Nibbles, bytes, words, and registers

A *nibble* is computer jargon for *four associated or contiguous bits* in the workspace of the computer; a nibble may be, for example, 1010B or 1111B or 0000B. A nibble can be thought of as representing one hex character.

A *byte* is *eight contiguous bits* in a computer; for example, 01011010B or 5AH is a byte.

A *word* is the 'normal' length or width of the workspace in a computer. Many microcomputers have a wordlength of eight bits or one byte; the 8086 has a wordlength of 16 bits. However, the 8088 has a wordlength of 16 bits *inside the central processor*, but it communicates with the outside world using an 8-bit wordlength (an advantage of this arrangement is that low-cost 8-bit support chips may be used by the computer, but it still has the powerful facilities provided by the 16-bit central processor architecture). Data may be stored in a microcomputer either in its memory or in a *register* in the central processor; the latter method of storage has some advantages over the former in that the register is in the microcomputer chip, whilst the memory is in a separate chip; this means that the data in the register can be accessed at a higher speed than the data in the memory. The 8086 and 8088 CPUs have an identical *architecture* or construction (see Chapter 2), and contain a range of 8-bit and 16-bit registers. In fact, certain pairs of 8-bit registers can be combined to form 16-bit registers for the purpose of arithmetic and other operations. Details of the registers are also provided in Chapter 2.

1.4   Binary addition

If the sum of two digits is less than the radix of the system, then the result is equal to the sum. If the sum is greater than the radix, then the addition produces a *carry-out*; this becomes the *carry-in* for the next higher-order addition. When adding two binary digits, the following possibilities exist:

$$0 + 0 = \text{sum of 0 and a carry-out of 0}$$
$$0 + 1 = \text{sum of 1 and a carry-out of 0}$$
$$1 + 0 = \text{sum of 1 and a carry-out of 0}$$
$$1 + 1 = \text{sum of 0 and a carry-out of 1}$$

However, the above calculations do not account for any carry-in from the next lower-order addition. A typical full binary addition is illustrated below.

```
augend, 5  =  0  1  0  1B
addend, 7  =  0  1  1  1B
              -------
carry-out      1  1  1
carry-in       1  1  1  0
              -------
sum            1  1  0  0B  =  CH  =  12
```

Consider the addition of the following 8-bit numbers

```
augend      11001010B    =    CAH
addend      01111010B    =    7AH
            -------            ---
sum         01000100B    =    44H
final carry    1                1
```

The result is an 8-bit *sum* of 44H and a *carry* of 1. The 'carry' is transferred to a one-bit memory known as a flip-flop or *flag*, which is one of the elements in a register in the microprocessor known as the *flags register*. Details of the flags register are given in Sections 1.8 and 1.11.

1.5   Binary subtraction

Computers carry out *subtraction* by a method known as *2s complement addition* as follows. Instead of subtracting the subtrahend from the minuend, it adds what is known as the 2s complement of the subtrahend to the minuend. The 2s complement of a binary number is evaluated using one of the following methods.

1. Complement the complete number, i.e., logically invert it and add '1' to the l.s.b.
2. Starting at the l.s.b., leave the bits unchanged *up to and including the first '1'*; complement the remaining bits.

Some examples of 8-bit numbers and their complements are given below.

	Binary value	2s complement
(a)	00000000	00000000
(b)	00000001	11111111
(c)	11111111	00000001
(d)	01010101	10101011

The 2s complement of a number can be thought of as the 'negative' value of the number. If we look at case (a) above, then $+0 = 00000000B$ and -0 (i.e., its 2s complement) = $00000000B$, that is $+0 = -0!$. In case (b), $+1 = 00000001B$ and $-1 = 11111111B$. In case (c), the binary value is 11111111 which, from case (b), is seen to be -1; the 2s complement of 11111111 is 00000001, i.e., $-(-1) = +1$. Finally in case (d), the 'negative' of 01010101 is seen to be 10101011.

To illustrate the way in which subtraction is performed by the computer, consider the case where unity is subtracted from seven. Using an 8-bit wordlength, the result is as follows:

$$+7 = \qquad 00000111B$$

$$-1 = \qquad 11111111B$$

$$\text{-------}$$

$$\text{result (ADD)} = \qquad 00000110B$$

$$\text{carry} = \qquad 1$$

The net result is $+6$ with a 'carry' from the m.s.b. of '1'. If the 'carry' is ignored, the result is correct; the 'carry', as we shall see in Section 1.8, is stored in the *carry flag* of the microcomputer, and is not necessarily part of the result.

1.6 Signed binary numbers

If, in an 8-bit computer, all eight bits are used to represent a number, then any number in the range 00000000 (zero) to 11111111 (255) can be represented. In this case we say that *unsigned numbers* (positive numbers) are being handled.

However, if we wish to handle *signed numbers*, i.e., both positive and negative numbers, the question which arises is 'how does the computer know the

Table 1.2

(a) 4-bit unsigned numbers		(b) 4-bit signed numbers	
Decimal	*Binary*	*Decimal*	*Binary*
15	1111	+7	0111
14	1110	+6	0110
13	1101	+5	0101
12	1100	+4	0100
11	1011	+3	0011
10	1010	+2	0010
9	1001	+1	0001
8	1000	0	0000
7	0111	−1	1111
6	0110	−2	1110
5	0101	−3	1101
4	0100	−4	1100
3	0011	−5	1011
2	0010	−6	1010
1	0001	−7	1001
0	0000	−8	1000

mathematical sign of the number?' The answer is that the computer works in 2s complement notation when handling signed numbers, and *the m.s.b. of the 'signed' number is used as a 'sign' bit* as follows:

If the m.s.b. = 0, the number is positive.

If the m.s.b. = 1, the number is negative.

This is verified by examples (b), (c), and (d) in Section 1.5. In cases (b) and (d), the original value is 'positive', and the 2s complement is negative. In case (c), the original value is negative and the 2s complement is positive, i.e., $-(-1) = +1$.

Consider the case of a computer using a 4-bit wordlength (see Table 1.2); the total number of code combinations is $2^4 = 16$. (*Note:* this applies whether signed or unsigned numbers are used.) In the case of unsigned numbers, the range stored is from zero (0000B) to 15 (1111B); no negative numbers are stored. In the case of signed numbers, all binary numbers having a '1' in the m.s.b. position are negative, so that the 4-bit computer can handle numbers in the range −8 (1000B) to +7 (0111B).

A simple method of determining the value of a signed number is by assuming that the m.s.b. has a *negative weighting* and the remainder of the number has a positive weighting, as shown in the following 4-bit signed binary values:

$$1011B \equiv -(1000B) + (011B) = -8 + 3 = -5$$

$$1101B \equiv -(1000B) + (101B) = -8 + 5 = -3$$

1.7 Sign extending a value

The 8086 and 8088 microprocessors can perform calculations using either 8-bit or 16-bit arithmetic. When a calculation has been performed using 8-bit signed arithmetic, and is needed later for a 16-bit calculation, it is necessary to *sign extend* the number into the highest byte when the 8-bit value is converted into a 16-bit value. For example, if the 8-bit result is $+2$ (00000010B), the 16-bit equivalent is obtained by filling the most significant byte with zeros; that is $62 = 0000000000000010$B. If the 8-bit result is -2 (11111110B), the corresponding 16-bit value is 1111111111111110B.

1.8 Microprocessor 'flags'

A *flag* is a memory element which is used to monitor or to 'flag' when a particular condition occurs in a microprocessor. Each microprocessor monitors a range of conditions, and the flags are grouped together in a register known as the *flags register* (or as the *status word*).

There are two types of flag, known respectively as *status flags* and *control flags*. Status flags record information about the result or status produced by the previous instruction(s). The status flags in the 8086 and 8088 microprocessors are

> the carry flag (CF)
> the parity flag (PF)
> the auxiliary carry flag (AF)
> the zero flag (ZF)
> the sign flag (SF)
> the overflow flag (OF)

The control flags are used to control the operation of the computer and are

> the trap flag (TF)
> the interrupt flag (IF)
> the direction flag (DF)

The 16-bit flags register in the 8086/88 chip is as shown in Fig. 1.1; unused bits are normally at logic '0'. The operation of the flags is as follows.

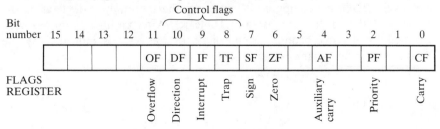

Figure 1.1 The 8086/88 flags register.

Carry flag: The CF is *set* (CF = 1) if there is a carry-out from the high-order bit for either an 8-bit or 16-bit arithmetic instruction. The CF is *cleared* (CF = 0) if there is no carry-out.

Parity flag: The PF is set when the *low-order* byte of a data operation has *even parity*, i.e., when the low-order byte has an even number of logic 1s in it. The PF is cleared when the low-order byte has *odd parity*, i.e., it has an odd number of logic 1s in it; remember, 'O' for Odd parity (see also Section 1.12).

Auxiliary carry flag: The state of this flag is equal to the carry-out from the low-order nibble of a calculation, i.e., the carry from bit b_3 to bit b_4 of the result of a calculation. This flag is used in decimal arithmetic operations (see Sections 1.9 and 1.11).

Zero flag: The ZF is set if the result of a data operation is zero. It is cleared if the result is non-zero.

Sign flag: The SF reflects the state of the m.s.b. of the result of an arithmetic operation (SF = 0 indicates a positive result, and SF = 1 indicates a negative result).

Trap flag: When this flag is set, the microprocessor is put into the single-step mode which can be used for 'debugging' purposes. In this mode, the microprocessor generates an 'internal' interrupt (see Chapter 9 for details) after each instruction is executed, and allows the user to inspect the state of the processor.

Interrupt flag: When this flag is set (see Chapter 9 for details), the microprocessor recognizes and accepts 'maskable' interrupt signals from external peripherals. When the IF is cleared, it does not accept these signals. The IF does not affect 'non-maskable' interrupts or 'internal' interrupts.

Direction flag: Setting the DF causes 'string' instructions to auto-decrement the 'source index' and 'destination index' registers (see Chapter 10 for details). Clearing the DF causes string instructions to auto-increment the source index and destination index registers.

Overflow flag: This flag is set when an arithmetic 'overflow' occurs (see also Section 1.11), that is, when a significant bit has been lost because the result of a *signed arithmetic* calculation exceeds the size of the destination location. An INTerrupt on Overflow instruction (mnemonic INTO) is available in the instruction set, and this generates an internal interrupt in this situation.

When studying the operation of the microprocessor using a debugging program such as DEBUG, the computer will print out the condition of the flags on the display monitor in the form listed in Table 1.3. After an instruction has been executed by the microcomputer, the state of the flags is indicated by the DEBUG utility program. A typical display is

NV UP DI NG NZ NA PE NC

and is interrupted as follows.

NV – a signed arithmetic overflow did not occur (OF = 0)
UP – the direction flag is cleared (DF = 0)

Table 1.3 Condition codes for flags (used by the DEBUG utility)

Flag	Bit number	Set	Cleared
Carry	0	CY	NC
Parity	2	PE (parity even)	PO (parity odd)
Auxiliary carry	4	AC (aux. carry)	NA (no aux. carry)
Zero	6	ZR (result zero)	NZ (result non-zero)
Sign	7	NG (NeGative)	PL (PLus)
Trap	8	This flag is not reported by DEBUG	
Interrupt	9	EI (Enable interrupt)	DI (Disable interrupt)
Direction	10	DN (DowN)	UP
Overflow	11	OV (OVerflow)	NV (No oVerflow)

DI – the maskable interrupts are disabled (IF $= 0$)
NG – the result is negative (SF $= 1$)
NZ – the result is non-zero (ZF $= 0$)
NA – there is no auxiliary carry (AF $= 0$)
PE – the parity of the result is even (PF $= 1$)
NC – there is no carry from the calculation (CF $= 0$)

1.9 Decimal arithmetic and the auxiliary carry flag

Although computers work in binary, a range of codes has been devised to enable it to perform decimal arithmetic. These are known as *binary-coded decimal (BCD) codes*, the most common being the *8421 BCD* code (see Table 1.4). In this code, each decimal digit is represented by four bits, or a nibble, the least significant bit having a decimal 'weighting' of '1' and the most significant bit having a weighting of '8'.

Table 1.4 8421 BCD code

Decimal value	8421 BCD code
0	0000
1	0001
2	0010
3	0011
4	0100
5	0101
6	0110
7	0111
8	1000
9	1001
Illegal code combinations	1010
	1011
	1100
	1101
	1110
	1111

Since the word length of a microcomputer is a multiple of eight bits, each byte in the computer can theoretically represent two decimal digits. There are, however, many codes which only allow eight bits to handle one decimal digit, and the situation is briefly discussed in Section 1.10. In this section we will concentrate on the use of the BCD code, which allows the computer to handle two decimal digits per byte.

Since four bits can represent up to sixteen different combinations of 1s and 0s, six of the code combinations are 'illegal' so far as the decimal system is concerned (see Table 1.4). It is therefore necessary for any decimal arithmetic process to bypass the illegal codes. The rule in microprocessors which enables it to perform decimal arithmetic is as follows:

If the sum of two numbers either
1. generates an illegal code, or
2. generates a 'carry' (known as an auxiliary carry)
    from the low-nibble of the byte,
then 6 (0110B) is added to the sum.

The 'extra' 0110B which is added to the answer is known as the *decimal adjustment* factor (there are two 'decimal adjustment' instructions in the instruction set of the 8086 and 8088 and are, respectively, *Decimal Adjustment for Addition* (whose mnemonic is DAA) and *Decimal Adjustment for Subtraction* (mnemonic DAS)).

Consider the following examples of decimal addition. The first example is 5 + 7, and the second is 9 + 9.

1.	decimal	BCD	Comment
	05	0000 0101	
	07	0000 0111	
	--	-------	
ADD	12	0000 1100	illegal code generated
		$\bigvee$	
		0	no auxiliary carry
ADD		0000 0110	decimal adjustment

		0001 0010	
		1 2	correct decimal solution

2.   decimal   BCD

          09   0000 1001

          09   0000 1001

          --   -------

ADD   18   0001 0010   legal code generated
                              \\/
                               1   auxiliary carry generated

ADD   0000 0110   decimal adjustment

                         0001 1000
                           ⌣   ⌣
                           1   8   correct solution

Example (1) produced an illegal code and Example (2) produced a carry from the low nibble of the sum. The auxiliary carry from bit 3 to bit 4 of the sum is stored in the *auxiliary carry flag* (AF) – see also Section 1.8.

1.10 Packed and unpacked binary codes

An 8-bit code which can handle two decimal digits is known as a *packed binary code*, the 8421 BCD code being an example of this kind.

An 8-bit code which can handle only one decimal digit is known as an *unpacked binary code*. One of the most widely used data transmission codes, the ASCII code (American Standard Code for Information Interchange) is an example of this kind. The instruction set of the 8086 and 8088 includes commands which allow you to perform decimal arithmetic on the ASCII code.

1.11 Arithmetic overflow

The *overflow flag* (OF) is set when a *signed arithmetic calculation* exceeds the storage capacity of the destination location. Consider for the moment the mathematical range of an 8-bit signed number; this is $+127$ to -128. If, for example, you add 10 to 120, the result of 130 is clearly 'out of range' if you are using signed arithmetic; in this case the OF will be 'set' to '1' by the computer. The internal mechanics of the above calculation are illustrated below.

$$10 = 0\ 0\ 0\ 0\ 1\ 0\ 1\ 0B$$

$$120 = 0\ 1\ 1\ 1\ 1\ 0\ 0\ 0B$$

----

sum   1 0 0 0 0 0 1 0B
           /\ \/
carry bits 0 1

Since the calculation is performed in signed arithmetic, the '1' in the m.s.b. position of the sum indicates that the result is negative! On the·face of it, $10 + 120 = -126$! This is clearly an error because the result has 'overflowed' the range of the 8-bit signed arithmetic values.

How then can the computer decide whether an overflow has occurred? It does so by *EXCLUSIVE-ORing* the carry from bit 6 with the carry from bit 7 (see the example above). If the result of this logical operation is '1', then an overflow has occurred, otherwise the result is correct.

In the above case, the carry from bit 6 is '1' and that from bit 7 is '0'; since they are not equivalent to one another, a signed arithmetic overflow has occurred and the OF is set.

1.12   An illustrative example of the use of flags

Consider the case where a microcomputer adds 04EDH to 0029H.

$$04EDH = 0\ 000\ 0100\ 1110\ 1101B$$

$$0029H = 0\ 000\ 0000\ 0010\ 1001B$$

non-zero result (NZ) ◄────┤ 0 000 0101 ┊0001 0110 ┊├───►three '1' bits (PO)

                                    0   0   1 ───► carry from bit 3 (AC)

no carry from m.s.b. (NC) └───►equivalent carry bits (NV)

             m.s.b. = 0 (PL)

The condition of each of the status flags *after the addition* is as follows (see also Section 1.8 and Table 1.3)

                    carry flag = 0 (NC)
                    parity flag = 0 (PO)
                    zero flag = 0 (NZ)
                    sign flag = 0 (PL)
                    overflow flag = 0 (NV)

1.13   Addressing a location in the memory of the computer

Each location within the memory of a computer contains unique data, and must therefore have its own 'address' within the system. The way in which a computer accesses a particular location is to put the electronic address on a set of lines known as the *address bus* (see Chapter 2 for details).

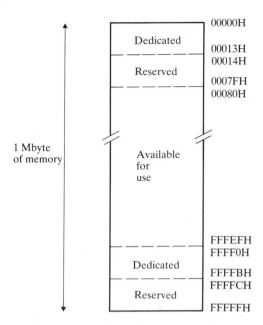

Figure 1.2   The memory map of the 8086/88 microcomputer.

The address consists of a number of 1s and 0s on the multi-line address bus (loosely analogous to the Post Code in the UK or the Zip Code in the US). A 16-bit microprocessor such as the 8086 and 8088 has 20 address bus lines and, since the memory is still accessed in byte form, then $2^{20} = 1\,048\,576$ bytes or 1 Mbyte of information is available. However, since the 8086 has a wordlength of 16 bits it can access, if so desired, 2^{19} words of information.

The range of memory addresses available to the 8086 and 8088 microprocessor starts at the 20-bit address 00000H and finishes at address FFFFFH; the *memory map* of the computer (see Fig. 1.2) shows the way in which the various addresses may be used. The addresses both at the bottom and the top of the memory map are either dedicated to specific functions or reserved by the Intel Corporation for use with hardware and software products. These areas of memory should only be used for the purposes specified by Intel; failure to do so may make the system incompatible with future developments of the 8086 and 8088 family.

1.14   Memory addressing and memory segmentation

You will see later (Chapter 2) that the 8086 and 8088 processors contain several 16-bit registers, but do not contain any 20-bit registers. The question which now arises is 'how can the 20-bit *physical address* of a location be deduced when only 16-bit registers are available?'

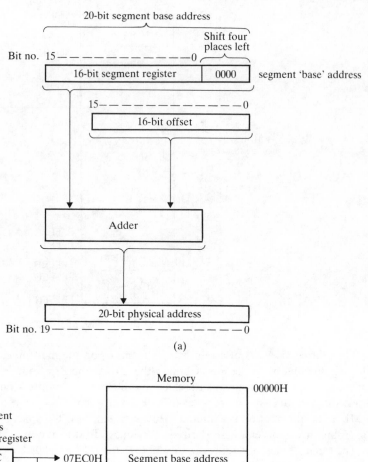

(a)

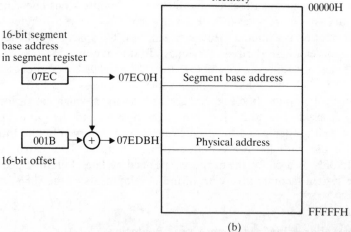

(b)

Figure 1.3 Determining the 20-bit physical address.

What the designers have in fact done is to designate certain registers as *segment registers*; these registers indicate the base address of a 'segment' in the memory (this is known as the *segment base*); a second 16-bit register is used to store the *offset* or *effective address* or *logical address* of the memory element within the segment. The segment base and the offset are combined in the manner described below to give the physical address of the required memory location. (*Note:* the segment base and the offset are unsigned values.)

The general arrangement for the management of memory addressing is shown in Fig. 1.3. The 20-bit segment base address is calculated by multiplying the 16-bit segment base address by 10H, i.e., the value in the segment register is shifted left four binary places (see Fig. 1.3(a)). The 16-bit offset value is added to the shifted base address to give the 20-bit physical address within the memory.

Figure 1.3(b) illustrates how the method is applied. In this diagram, the segment register contains 07ECH; the corresponding 20-bit segment base address is

$$07ECH \times 10H = 07EC0H$$

If the 16-bit offset is 001BH, the physical address of the memory location is calculated as follows:

$$physical\ address = 20\text{-bit segment base address} + 16\text{-bit offset}$$

$$= 07EC0H + 001BH = 07EDBH$$

Since the offset can have any value in the range 0000H to FFFFH, i.e., up to 64K of memory, the segment has a 'length' of 64K. In the above case, the address of the 'top' of the segment is

$$07EC0H + FFFFH = 17EBFH$$

The computer can therefore access any location within the 64K segment commencing at address 07EC0H.

1.15 Segment registers in the 8086 and 8088

The 64K bytes of addresses available in each segment is, in fact, only a small proportion of the 1 Mbyte of memory which is available to the microcomputer. Although it is, of course, possible to access a larger range of addresses by changing the 16-bit segment base value, the Intel Corporation have simplified matters by placing four segment registers at your disposal. That is, four 64K byte segments can be used in any one program without changing the segment base address.

The segment registers are known respectively as the *code segment (CS) register*, the *stack segment (SS) register*, the *data segment (DS) register*, and the *extra segment (ES) register*. Each of these registers is loaded with a 16-bit value;

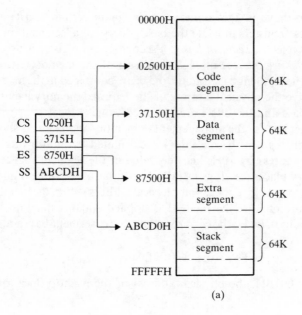

(a)

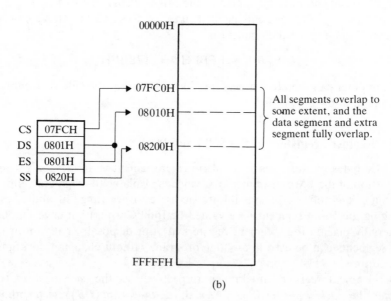

(b)

Figure 1.4 (a) Maximum simultaneous access of memory; (b) overlapping segments.

the computer automatically multiplies each one by 10H to 'point' at the base address of a segment of memory. Examples of memory access are illustrated in Fig. 1.4.

In Fig. 1.4(a), each segment is separated from the next by a gap, giving the maximum possible simultaneous memory access of 4×64Kbytes. Figure 1.4(b) shows a simpler case in which all the segments overlap to some extent, and the DS and ES fully overlap.

2
Microprocessor-based computer systems

2.1 Introduction to digital computers

A *digital computer* is a versatile calculating machine which can perform many operations at high speed under the control of a *program* stored in the *memory* of the machine. A block diagram of a typical microprocessor-based computing system is shown in Fig. 2.1.

The *microprocessor chip*, which is the *central processing unit* (CPU), contains three very important elements, namely

1. The *control unit*, which sends signals to all parts of the computer to coordinate and control their operation.
2. The *arithmetic and logic unit* (ALU), which performs all the arithmetic and logical functions of the computer. In the 8086 and 8088 CPUs these include adding, subtracting, multiplying, dividing, ANDing, ORing, EXCLUSIVE-ORing, complementing, shifting and rotating data.
3. The registers, which can be used to store data. These registers include the flags register and the segment registers mentioned in Chapter 1. The CPU also contains several *general-purpose registers*, which are often used as a *scratch-pad memory* in which data is temporarily stored during some calculations.

There are two broad categories of main memory, namely *read-only memory* (*ROM*) and *random-access memory* (*RAM*).

A ROM contains data which cannot normally be changed by the user and can, therefore, only be read by the computer. The data in the RAM can both be read and/or altered by the user, i.e., it is a read–write memory; the expression 'random access' means that any location within the memory can be accessed at random by the computer. However, it is also the case that any location in a ROM can be accessed at random; none the less, the term RAM is reserved in computer jargon to mean a 'read–write' memory.

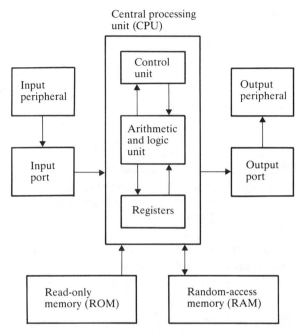

Figure 2.1 A microprocessor-based computing system.

The program which controls the operation of the computer is known as the *operating system*, and it is the operating system which is activated when power is applied to the computer. A ROM is a *non-volatile memory*, that is, it does not lose its stored data when the computer is switched off; at switch-on, the operating system in ROM causes the computer to initialize the system so that, for example, a message is printed on the screen of the monitor and the various peripheral devices such as printers, etc., are correctly initialized.

A RAM is a *volatile memory*, and it 'loses' the stored data when the supply is switched off; when power is restored, the RAM contains electronic 'garbage'. In a small system such as a traffic-light controller, the RAM requirement is fairly small (possibly less than 1 Kbyte), and is used as a scratch-pad memory to store temporary data such as the direction in which traffic is flowing. In a personal computer (such as the IBM PC), the user may need it to develop fairly large programs and, in this case, the RAM capacity of the computer may have to be quite large.

There are, of course, many other types of memory in use with computers, including magnetic tapes, disks, drums and bubble memories, together with optical memories and charge-coupled device memories.

The range of peripherals which may be connected to a computer is very wide, and is broadly divided into *input peripherals* and *output peripherals*. An input peripheral supplies or 'inputs' data to the computer; a simple example of an input peripheral is a switch or sensor, a more complex peripheral being a magnetic disk reader. An output peripheral is one which accepts data from the computer; a lamp can be thought of as a simple output peripheral, a more complex example being an 'intelligent' printer. Some peripherals contain both input and output devices, a computer terminal being an example of this kind; this contains a keyboard (an input device) and a monitor (an output device).

Both input and output peripherals are connected to the CPU by a *port* (see Fig. 2.1), which is a specialized integrated circuit chip. A *dedicated port* is one which can pass data in one direction only, i.e., it is either an input port or it is an output port. Many systems use *programmable ports* which can, according to the needs of the system, be programmed to operate either an an input port or as an output port; in most cases, the ports can be programmed to handle both input data and output data. Examples of the use of programmable ports can be found in Chapters 7–9.

Many of the input/output ports (described as I/O ports) are complex; typically, a programmable I/O 'port' may contain not only several independent ports, but also RAM, or ROM, or programmable timer(s).

2.2   The 8088 chip and the three-bus system

Figure 2.2 shows the pin-out of the Intel 8088 chip. The chip has 40 connection pins, but the sophistication of the chip is such that 40 pins are not sufficient to meet its needs! To overcome this problem, the designers have used many of the pins for two purposes. That is, at one moment in time, one of the pins may be used to convey, say, data to the system and at another time the same pin may be used to convey part of the 'address' of a memory location to the system. This technique is known as *multiplexing*.

Microprocessor-based systems operate around a *three-bus system*, each 'bus' containing a number of lines along which signals travel. The buses are known respectively as the address bus, the data bus and the control bus. Referring to Fig. 2.2, you will see that pins 9–16, inclusive, of the 8088 chip are multiplexed; that is, one moment they carry address bus signals, and the next moment they are used for data (hence the use of the terminology AD in association with these pins – A for 'address' bus and D for 'data' bus). Line AD0 is the least significant line of the AD bus and AD7 is the most significant line. You will also note that some of the remaining address bus lines are multiplexed with the control bus (see pins 35–38 inclusive).

The purpose of the *data bus* is to carry data both into and out of the CPU. In general, there are as many lines in the data bus as there are bits in the wordlength of the CPU. Whilst this is true in the case of the 8086, the 8088 CPU differs from other CPUs in that the width of the data bus 'external' to the CPU is 8 bits, whilst the CPU is itself capable of 'internally' handling 16 bits. Hence

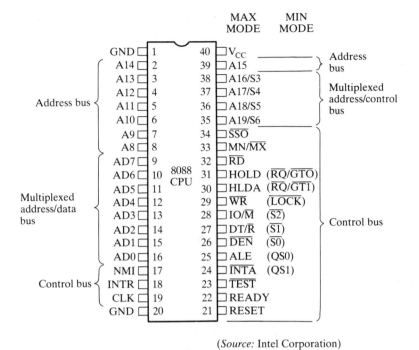

(*Source:* Intel Corporation)

Figure 2.2 The 8088 chip (*Source*: Intel Corporation).

the 'external' data bus of the 8088 needs only 8 lines (the 8086 has an external 16-bit word length and needs 16 lines in it).

The data bus is *bidirectional*, that is, data can travel either from the CPU to a peripheral, or in the reverse direction. (*Note:* At any one point in time, the data travels in one direction only.)

The number of memory locations that may be addressed by a CPU having N lines in the address bus is 2^N; in order to address 1 Mbyte of data, the *address bus* needs to have 20 lines in it. The low byte of the information on the address bus (which is carried on lines A0–A7, inclusive) is multiplexed with the data bus as described above, to give the AD lines on the chip. Address bus lines A8–A15, inclusive, are not multiplexed (see Fig. 2.2), and lines A16–A19, inclusive, are multiplexed with some lines in the control bus.

Generally the signals on the address bus travel from the CPU to the support chips. If, for example, the CPU wishes to access data from the memory address 178ABH, it puts the 20-bit binary pattern 0001 0111 1000 1010 1011 on the address bus lines; the m.s.b., i.e., '0', is placed on address line A19, and the l.s.b., i.e., '1', is placed on address line A0.

The problem which arises now is 'how does the system know when an address is on the AD pins, and when is data on them?' This question is answered when we look at the control bus.

The purpose of the *control bus* signals is to control and coordinate the operation of the support chips, all of which are necessary for the correct performance of the microcomputer. For example, when the CPU wishes to read data from memory address 178ABH it must, firstly, tell the system that it is about to put the address on the address bus. The way in which the CPU advises the system that this is about to happen is to drive the ALE pin (pin 25) high (Address Latch Enable); the system is then aware that the AD-bus lines carry address information. Later, when the AD bus lines carry data, the ALE pin has a logic '0' on it (other control bus lines may also be involved).

There are many other lines in the control bus including, for example, the line which tells the system that the CPU is ready to read data from a location, and the line which tells the system that it is ready to write data to a location.

Whilst the control bus is unidirectional, each line is dedicated to transmitting data either from the CPU or to the CPU. For example, the ALE control bus line is a dedicated output line, that is, it carries information from the CPU to the system. On the other hand, the INTR line (pin 18) is a dedicated input line, which is used to carry an INTeRrupt request signal from the system to the CPU (see Chapter 9 for information about interrupts).

When referring to Fig. 2.2, you will see that, depending on whether the CPU is in its *MIN MODE* or in its *MAX MODE*, a number of the control bus pins perform alternative functions. The 8086 and 8088 are complex chips, and one way of simplifying the hardware design of the system is to cause the CPU to 'hold back' some of its control functions; this allows a simple system to operate with the MINimum number of control functions. Whether a system operates in the MIN mode or the MAX mode depends on the logic level connected to the MN/$\overline{\text{MX}}$ pin (pin 33). In any given system, this pin is permanently connected either to a logic '1' level (MIN mode) or to logic '0' (MAX mode).

When the CPU is in its MAX mode, a chip known as the *8288 bus controller* is brought into use. This chip performs many of the functions of the control pins on the CPU, leaving the control pins on the CPU to perform other functions. For example, the function of the ALE pin in the CPU (pin 25 in the MIN mode) is produced by the 8255 chip, leaving pin 25 on the CPU to perform a function which was 'hidden' when in the MIN mode. The MAX mode is implemented when the 8086 and 8088 are used in connection with medium-to-large processing systems.

2.3   A simple 8088 system

Figure 2.3 illustrates a simple system which is used to read data from sensors V and W and, after processing the data, sends signals to lamps X, Y and Z. The

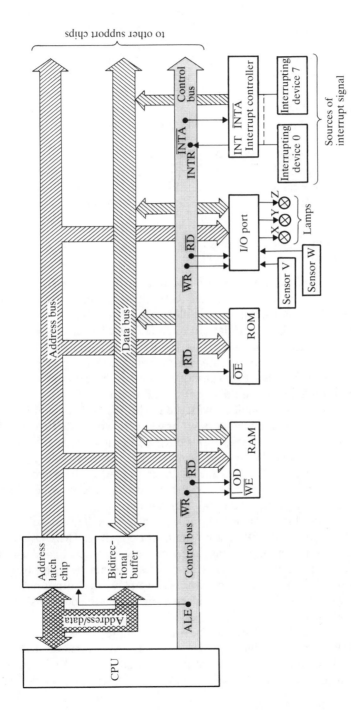

Figure 2.3 Block diagram of a microprocessor-based system using an 8088.

program controlling the system would be stored in ROM (in this case the RAM is used as a scatch-pad memory to store the data from the sensors and as an area of memory in which the results of calculations are stored). The figure also illustrates the interconnections between the support chips and the 3-bus system.

As mentioned in Section 2.2, part of the address bus is multiplexed with the data bus. The purpose of the *address latch* chip is, when ALE goes 'high', to latch or 'save' the 20-bit address of the next item of data required by the CPU. This enables the 20-bit address to be held on the address bus as long as it is required.

If the required address is in ROM, it is accessed as follows. The ROM chip has a pin on it designated $\overline{OE}$; this is interpreted as 'the Output from the chip is Enabled whenever the OE pin is driven low', i.e., it is enabled when a logic '0' is applied to it. In order to read data from the ROM chip, two conditions must be satisfied:

1. the address must be on the address bus,
2. the output from the chip must be 'enabled'.

The first condition has already been satisfied in the manner described above. The second condition is satisfied when the $\overline{RD}$ control bus line is driven low (see also Fig. 2.2); this control bus line (called the READ line) is driven low whenever the CPU needs to read data from an address. Hence, when the CPU receives an instruction to read data from the ROM, it automatically satisfies conditions 1 and 2 above, and the data is read from the location in ROM. The reading process is non-destructive, causing a 'copy' of the data in the specified address to be transferred along the data bus and into the CPU.

If the CPU needs to communicate with the RAM, the CPU must inform the RAM whether it needs to read data from it or wants to write data to it. The $\overline{RD}$ and $\overline{WR}$ control bus lines are used for this purpose. As described earlier, during a memory read period, the $\overline{RD}$ line is driven low; during a memory write period, the $\overline{WR}$ line (known as the WRITE line) is driven low. Also, these two lines are never driven low simultaneously; that is, the RAM chip can never be told that it must simultaneously accept data and transmit data.

If data is to be read from the RAM, the CPU drives the $\overline{RD}$ control bus line low; this, in turn, drives the OD pin on the RAM chip low. The OD pin is an active high 'Output buffer Disable' pin, and when this pin is held high the output buffer amplifiers in the chip are disabled, and data cannot be 'read' from the chip. Hence, when the $\overline{RD}$ control bus line is driven low, the output buffers are enabled and the data in the specified address is placed on the data bus lines for the CPU to read.

On the other hand, if the CPU needs to write data to a specified address in RAM, the $\overline{WR}$ control bus line is driven low (at the same time the $\overline{RD}$ line is held high, disabling the output buffer of the RAM chip). The $\overline{WR}$ control line is connected to the $\overline{WE}$ pin (Write Enable) of the RAM; when the $\overline{WE}$ pin is driven low, the input buffers of the RAM chip are enabled, allowing the data which the CPU has placed on the data bus to be stored in the specified address in the RAM.

Should the program instructions cause the CPU to communicate with the I/O port it must, as before, put the address of the port on the address bus. As with the RAM, data from sensors V and W are read from the input port when the $\overline{\text{RD}}$ control bus line is driven low by the CPU (this occurs when the CPU executes an INput instruction – see Chapter 7 for details). Data is written to the output port, i.e., data is sent to lamps X, Y and Z, when the $\overline{\text{WR}}$ control bus line is driven low (this happens when the computer executes an OUTput instruction). If you study 'timing' diagrams of microprocessors, you will find that the CPU only puts data on the data bus for a fraction of a microsecond, and it is usually the case that the output port contains 'latches' or memory elements, allowing it to latch or hold the data within the port after the data has been removed from the data bus. If this were not the case, the data would be 'lost', and would not be displayed on the lamps.

It was mentioned earlier that the main program can be 'interrupted' by a large number of devices (see Chapter 9 for a full description of interrupts). These may typically include a keyboard, or a disk drive, or a printer, etc. In the 8086 and 8088 family, the hardware interrupt connections are generally handled by an interrupt controller chip – see Fig. 2.3). When a device such as a keyboard needs to interrupt the main program, it applies a signal to the interrupt controller which, in turn, drives its INT pin high. This is connected to the INTR control bus line on the CPU and, on the completion of each instruction cycle, the CPU tests the INTR line to see if it has been driven high. When it discovers a logic '1' on this line, it issues an INTerrupt Acknowledge signal by driving the $\overline{\text{INTA}}$ control bus line low; in turn, this drives the $\overline{\text{INTA}}$ pin on the interrupt controller chip low. When the CPU has acknowledged receipt of the interrupt request signal in this way, the interrupt controller chip places a binary value on the data bus which is known as the *interrupt type number*; this is an 8-bit value in the range 00H–FFH (or 0–255). The CPU then reads the interrupt type number from the data bus, and causes program control to be transferred to a specific address in the memory which handles the type of interrupt requested by that interrupt type number (see Chapter 9 for details).

You will notice in Fig. 2.3 that the interrupt controller is not connected to the address bus. The reason is that, once the CPU has acknowledged the interrupt, it is the interrupt controller which issues the information (which is the interrupt type number) from which the address of the interrupting source is calculated.

The methods of dealing with the hardware connections to the interrupting sources are many and varied, but the interrupt controller is one of the most popular. Each controller can only handle eight interrupt sources, but they can be cascaded to handle multiples of eight interrupting sources, so that a system may typically have up to $8 \times 8 = 64$ interrupting sources.

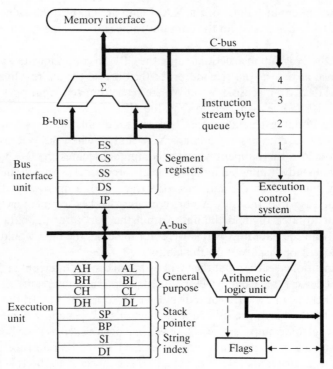

Figure 2.4   Architecture of the 8088 (*Source*: Intel Corporation).

2.4   Architecture of the 8088 chip

A simplified architecture or 'structure' of the 8088 chip is shown in Fig. 2.4. Data is moved between the CPU and the main memory by means of the *memory interface*, and any incoming information which is part of an instruction is placed in the *instruction stream byte queue*. The instruction at the head of this queue is passed to the *execution unit* (EU), which executes the instruction.

Even as this happens, the *bus interface unit* (BIU) is all the time trying to fill the instruction stream byte queue. This is known as *pipelined architecture*, and ensures that an instruction is available for execution. Other types of CPU wait until an instruction has been executed before it fetches the next instruction; for this reason, the 8086 and 8088 chips tend to be (for the same clock frequency) faster in operation than other CPUs.

You will also see that the BIU contains the four 16-bit segment registers described in Chapter 1, together with the 16-bit instruction Pointer register (IP).

The EU contains a number of 8-bit and 16-bit general-purpose registers which can be used in a variety of ways together with the ALU. It also contains the flags register mentioned in Chapter 1.

2.5 The 8088 registers

Referring to Fig. 2.4, you will see that the BIU contains five 16-bit registers, namely the four segment registers and the IP register. The latter register performs a similar function to the program counter register in most other microprocessors, and it 'points' to the address of the next instruction within the code segment to be executed by the CPU. The use of the segment registers is described below.

CS – This stores the base address of the *code segment*, i.e., the memory segment where the machine code version of the program is stored. The value in this register is combined with the number in the IP in the manner outlined in Section 1.14 to give the address of the next instruction to be executed.

SS – This stores the base address of the *stack segment* in the memory of the computer.

DS – This contains the starting address of the *data segment*, which is the area of memory holding the data for the program.

ES – This is the *extra segment* register which is used to point to an 'extra' or additional segment in memory which can be used for data.

The registers in the EU are as follows. There are four 16-bit general-purpose registers (AX, BX, CX and DX), each of which can be used as two 8-bit registers thus:

$$AX = AH \text{ and } AL \qquad BX = BH \text{ and } BL$$

$$CX = CH \text{ and } CL \qquad DX = DH \text{ and } DL$$

where H and L respectively refer to the 'High byte and 'Low' byte. The 'A' register is sometimes referred to as the *accumulator* register, and is used by many instructions.

The 16-bit *stack pointer* register (SP) 'points' to the 'top' of an area of memory known as the 'stack' (see also the SS register); the 16-bit *base pointer* register (BP) 'points' to the 'bottom' of the memory stack; the latter register can also be used as another general-purpose register (but the SP register is dedicated to a specific purpose).

There are two 16-bit registers known as *string index* registers which are used to point at 'strings' of data in the memory. These registers are the *source index* register (SI) and the *destination index* register (DI); they can also be used as general-purpose 16-bit registers.

Finally, there is the 16-bit *flags register* (FR), which stores the condition of the CPU 'flags', and was introduced in Chapter 1. Only nine of the sixteen bits of the register are used for flags, the others being unused.

3
Introduction to assembly language programming

This chapter introduces the fundamental concepts of assembly language programming and, once understood, you will be in a position to study the full-length programs described in later chapters.

3.1 The BIOS and the DOS

When an 8088-based personal computer is switched on, it initially reads data from the disk currently in the disk drive and, if this is the system disk, the computer asks you for the date and the time. We will now look into what causes this to happen and what effect it has on the use of the memory.

Every 8088-based personal computer has two very important elements in its make-up, namely the *Basic Input/Output System* (BIOS) and the *Disk Operating System* (DOS).

The BIOS is a program stored in the ROM (and is located at the 'top' of the memory map), and when the computer is first turned on, control is transferred to the BIOS. This program initializes the computer and looks for information from the DOS. The latter is a control program which manages the resources of the computer such as the disk system and the memory. At switch-on, the BIOS 'boots up' or *bootstraps* the DOS, and reads a predefined part of the disk into its memory.

The DOS sets up certain entries in the *interrupt service vector table* at the bottom of the RAM (see Chapter 9 for details). The memory map of the computer both before and after bootstrapping is shown in diagrams (a) and (b) of Fig. 3.1. The 8088 system is designed to make intensive use of interrupts as a means of controlling the operation of the computer. Interrupts were briefly introduced in Chapter 2, and are discussed in detail in Chapter 9. The BIOS and

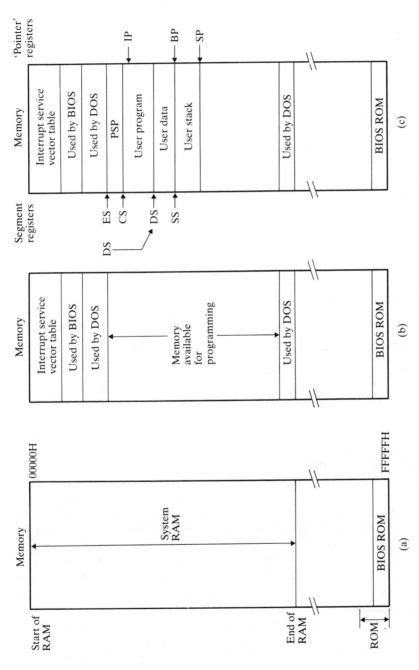

Figure 3.1 The memory map of the 8088 at various points in its operation: (a) before bootstrap; (b) after bootstrap; (c) user program loaded.

the DOS also use up further areas of the RAM on the memory map, as shown in Fig. 3.1(b).

When you have written and entered an assembly program into the memory of the computer, more of the available memory is taken up as shown in Fig. 3.1(c). The *program segment prefix* (PSP) contains information about the program, and is used as an interface with the DOS. Above this in the memory of the computer lie certain areas which are designated in the program, including the user program itself (which is in the code segment of the memory), the user data (depending on the program, this part either may or may not be needed), and the user stack (which is in the stack segment). In addition, there may be an 'extra' segment in the memory (often used in connection with strings and similar applications – see Chapter 10 for details).

The DOS initially causes the DS and ES registers to 'point' to the beginning of the PSP. If the program requires the use of a data segment and/or an extra segment, *it is the programmer's responsibility to set up the DS and ES registers to 'point' to the start of the respective segments*. A method of doing this is described in Section 3.10.

The DOS also causes the CS register to 'point' to the start of the code segment, and causes the SS register to 'point' to the start of the stack segment, and the BP register to point to the 'bottom' of the stack.

3.2   Writing and running an assembly language program

When creating an assembly language program that can be run or 'executed', several steps must be carried out in the sequence shown in Fig. 3.2.

Initially, you need to load the *line editor program*, EDLIN, into the memory of the computer, and type in the assembly language program. EDLIN enables you to edit the program or 'file', that is to make additions, deletions, alterations, etc. When you load EDLIN into the memory of the computer, you will need to declare the 'name' of the file; we will call it FILE_1. The EDLIN utility is a simple but specialized form of word processor; it is possible to use a more sophisticated form of word processor such as WORDSTAR for the purpose of editing your program. When you have typed the program into the computer, you have created what is known as the *source file* or source program. EDLIN also lets you save it on a disk exactly as it has been typed. However, it does not attempt to correct any syntax errors – this comes in the next stage. The source file is saved on the disk as FILE_1.ASM; the '.ASM' part of the filename is described as the filename *extension*. The files created at various stages have differing extensions.

Next you load the *assembler program* (ASM or ASM86), which is used to convert the source file (in ASCII code) into the machine code *object file*. The object file is saved on the disk as FILE_1.OBJ; other files may be created at this time (all having the name FILE_1, but having different extensions). The assembler

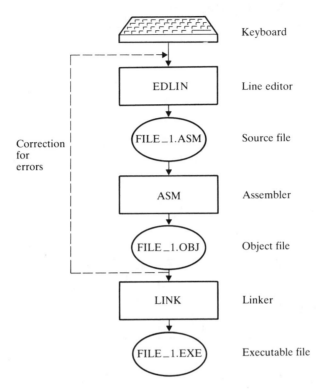

Figure 3.2 Creating an executable file.

detects syntax errors in the instructions and directives, but does not discover errors in 'comments' you have made in the program documentation. It will print out the errors on the monitor screen, and you will have to go back to EDLIN to correct them (see the dotted line link in Fig. 3.2). When you have corrected all the errors you can find, you must call up ASM once more to create a new object file to replace the original object file. If further errors occur, you must repeat the EDLIN–ASM loop again.

If errors do occur, a fairly quick method of finding out where they are in the program is to display the file FILE_1.LST (which can be created at the same time that you produce FILE_1.OBJ); this lists the assembly language program together with any errors associated with it. The operation manual of the computer provides information about the '.LST' file.

Having cleared up any syntax errors, you load the linker program LINK into the memory of the computer. This converts the object file into the *executable file* FILE_1.EXE, which can be loaded and run by the DOS. Once again, other files may be created at this time.

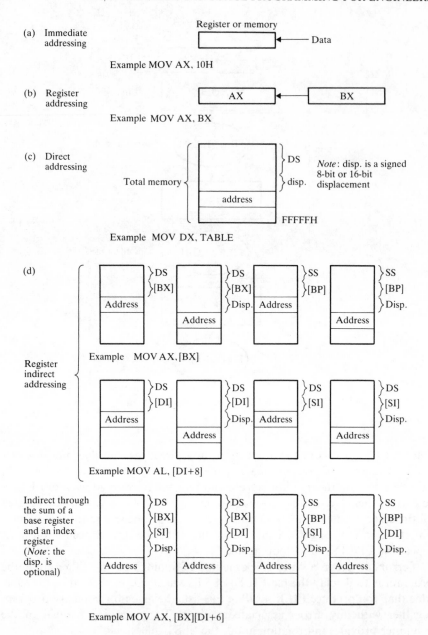

Figure 3.3 Addressing modes.

An executable file, once created, may be run either one step at a time using the DEBUG utility program or in its entirety.

3.3   Addressing modes

Addressing modes are the ways in which the computer can address or locate an operand or number. The 8088 has a wide variety of addressing modes, which are summarized in Fig. 3.3.

Operands which *are not in the memory of the computer*, i.e., not in the RAM or the ROM, use either immediate addressing or register addressing. *Immediate addressing* contains the operand in the instruction itself and is illustrated in Fig. 3.3(a) for the case of the instruction

MOV AX,10H

which MOVes immediately into register AX the value 10H. The operand, 10H, is seen to be in the instruction.

In *register addressing* (see Fig. 3.3(b)), the operand is contained in a register in the CPU rather than in the memory of the computer. The register addressing instruction

MOV AX,BX

causes the CPU to 'MOVe into register AX a copy of the data in register BX'. Immediate addressing and register addressing are processed more quickly than other addressing mode instructions (see below), because all other forms of addressing mode call on the CPU to compute the full 20-bit address of the operand.

The concept of the *effective address* (EA) of a location is used in the 8088, and is the *displacement* or *offset* in bytes of the address of the operand from the *beginning of the segment* (i.e., the address calculated from the value in the segment register).

Operands which *are in the memory of the computer* can be accessed using either direct addressing or indirect addressing; in both cases, the CPU must evaluate the full 20-bit address of the operand. *Direct addressing* (see Fig. 3.3(c)) uses a 16-bit EA, i.e., an offset or displacement as shown by the following instruction.

MOV DX,TABLE

This instruction MOVes a constant (which is named or *labelled* TABLE at an earlier point in the program) from the memory (hence the need for a 20-bit address) into register DX. This is illustrated in the direct addressing example in Fig. 3.3 and, unless instructed otherwise, the DS register is used to store the base address of the segment in which TABLE is stored. In fact any of the four segment registers could be used (i.e., DS, CS, ES or SS) and, should you want to use the ES register rather than the DS register, the instruction would be written

MOV DX,ES:TABLE

where ES is known as the *segment override prefix* for the instruction. The value in ES is used in this case in association with TABLE to compute the 20-bit physical address.

In *indirect addressing* (see Fig. 3.3(d)) the *address of the data*, rather than the data itself, is in the memory location specified by the instruction. There are many ways of implementing indirect addressing, and the two broad categories used by the 8088 are shown in Fig. 3.3, and described below.

REGISTER INDIRECT ADDRESSING

The 16-bit offset address within a segment is contained either in a base register or an index register, i.e., in one of the registers BX, BP, SI or DI. An example of this type of addressing is

MOV AX,[BX]

This instruction MOVes the data at the address calculated from the value in the segment register and in the BX register, into register AX. If DS contains 0800H and BX contains 0006H, the data at the physical address (08000 + 0006) = 08006H is moved into AL.

Optionally, register indirect addressing may also have an additional displacement:

MOV AL,[BX + 2]

In this case the total offset within the segment is BX + 2 = 0006 + 2 = 0008H. Yet another example of this addressing mode is

MOV AX,TEST[DI]

where TEST is an offset which has been specified at another point in the program, and the total offset within the segment is

TEST + content of register DI

The [ ] brackets can be thought of in this context as meaning '+'.

INDIRECT THROUGH A BASE REGISTER AND AN INDEX REGISTER

This addressing mode uses the contents of two registers to determine the 16-bit offset to be used in the calculation of the 20-bit physical address. An example of this type of instruction is

MOV AX,[BX][SI]

The offset or EA of the required location is the 16-bit sum BX + SI. This addressing mode can, optionally, be used with a displacement as follows:

MOV AX,[BX][SI + 2]

3.4 Instructions and directives

The source program contains two types of statement, namely instructions and directives (the latter has the alternative names of *pseudo-instructions*, *pseudo-operations*, or *pseudo-ops*).

An *instruction* is written in *mnemonic* form as follows:

MOV DS,AX

Each instruction is translated into machine code form by the assembler, and can be acted on by the computer. A *directive* or pseudo-op (see also Section 3.10) is recognized by the CPU as a piece of advisory information, and is *not converted into machine code*. Each directive gives advice about such things as the type of data currently being handled, or that the end of a segment or procedure has been reached, etc. Widely used pseudo-ops include

DB   Define Byte(s)
DW   Define Word(s)
SEGMENT   define SEGMENT
ENDS   END of Segment
PROC   define PROCedure
ENDP   END of Procedure
ASSUME   establish segment register addressability
EQU   EQUate directive
END   END of assembly language program

3.5 Assembly language format

An assembly language instruction is written in *fields* or columns as in Table 3.1. The reason for each field is described later in the chapter, but a few general comments are in order here. Of the over, only the START label is associated with a program instruction, the other labels being linked with directives or pseudo-ops.

Table 3.1 Fields used in assembly language

Label or name	Instruction, directive or mnemonic	Operand(s)	Comment
MY_STACK	SEGMENT	PARA STACK	;initialize STACK segment
MY_DATA	ENDS		;end of STACK segment
START:	MOV	AX,MY_DATA	;begin to initialize DATA segment
	DAA		;Decimal Adjust the result for Addition
MY_CODE	ENDS		;end of code segment
	END	START	;end of assembly language program

Of the four fields, only the mnemonic field is mandatory, the others being optional (however, in some cases the operand field is associated with the mnemonic field and, in such cases, the latter is mandatory).

The fields must be separated from one another by at least one blank space, and the *comment field must be preceded by a semicolon* (this applies even if the comment is on a line on its own.)

3.6   The label field

This assigns a *symbolic name* to the program line, enabling the program to refer to the instruction by name rather than by a line number. The assembler program calculates the effective address of the labelled line, and this is used later when the label is referred to by the program. Each label must be continuous and must not contain spaces; a label can be split into sections by means of an underscore character, e.g., MY_CODE.

A *colon* is used between a label and an instruction when the instruction refers to an item *inside the same segment as itself*. For example

LOOP_4:   ROL   AL,1   ;'rotate' contents of AL left

However, a colon is never used between a label and a directive, as shown below.

MY_STACK   SEGMENT   PARA STACK

Labels can be used to make a program more readable. For example, the following program line

TABLE   EQU   [CX][DI]

makes the effective address of a TABLE in the memory of the computer EQUal to the sum (CX + DI). When the CPU meets the instruction

          MOV   AL,TABLE

it moves the data in the effective address TABLE into register AL. This is equivalent to the less readable instruction

          MOV   AL,[CX][DI]

3.7   The mnemonic field

This holds a two- to six-letter acronym or abbreviation of an instruction. Thus

MOV means MOVe data from one location to another
INC means INCrement the content of a register or memory
SUB means SUBtract one number from another

A full list of mnemonics is given in the appendix. The mnemonic informs the assembler program not only what type of operation is about to be performed, but also how many operands it should obtain from the operand field.

3.8   The operand field

The information in this field tells the CPU where to find the data which is to be operated on by the computer. For example, the instruction

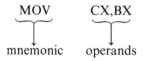

tells the computer to MOVe a *copy* of the data in register BX into register CX. In a two-operand instruction, as in the above case, the operands are separated from one another by a comma. The first operand (CX in the above case) is known as the *destination operand*, the second operand being known as the *source operand*. The instruction can be represented as follows:

$$(CX) \leftarrow (DX)$$

where the parenthesis '( )' is a shorthand way of writing 'the contents of'. The source operand is not altered by the execution of the instruction, but the destination operand may be altered. For example, if CX contains 89ABH and DX contains 1256H, the MOV CX,DX instruction results in the contents of DX remaining unchanged, but causes the value in CX to change to 1256H.

3.9   The comment field

The information in this field makes the program more user-friendly and understandable. The comment field must be preceded by a semicolon, and the comments in the field are not converted into machine code by the assembler. For example, the comment on the following line explains the purpose of the instruction

MOV CX,DX ;MOVE (DX) INTO (CX)

A comment can be included as a stand-alone item or, alternatively, it can be used to include a short paragraph in the program to properly document it, as indicated below.

```
;**** A COMMENT ****
;,,,,,,,,,,,,,,,,,,,,
;THIS IS A PARAGRAPH
;IN THE FORM OF A COMMENT
;*************************
```

3.10   Pseudo-ops or directives

Pseudo-ops give 'directions' to the assembler, and are used for many purposes including allocating memory space, defining symbols, and other 'housekeeping' functions. Each pseudo-op may have up to four fields as follows

Label   Pseudo-op   Operand   Comment

Only the pseudo-op field is mandatory, the others being optional. As with an instruction, a pseudo-op can be placed anywhere on a line, but must be separated by at least one blank space from any other field.

ASM-86 has several directive statements or pseudo-ops, including *data definition* pseudo-ops, *symbol definition* pseudo-ops, *segment definition* pseudo-ops, *procedure definition* pseudo-ops, *termination* pseudo-ops, and *external reference* pseudo-ops.

DATA DEFINITION PSEUDO-OPS

A data definition pseudo-op allocates memory space for an item or items of data; it associates a label with the memory address. For example, the pseudo-ops DB, DW and DD allocate a byte, a word, and a double-word, respectively, as follows:

```
ONE_BYTE   DB   (?)    ;allocates one byte
ONE_WORD   DW   (0H)   ;allocates one word (two bytes)
BIG_WORD   DD   (?)    ;allocates a double-word (four bytes)
```

ONE_BYTE is the symbolic address associated with a byte memory location allocated in the data segment, the value initially stored in the byte being initially unknown, that is it contains electronic 'garbage'. ONE_WORD allocates two consecutive bytes in memory, both bytes initially containing 00H. BIG_WORD allocates two words or four consecutive bytes in memory, whose value is initially unknown. If an item of data must have a specific value, it can also be defined by a data definition pseudo-op as follows:

TEST DB 30   ;allocates one byte in memory to data labelled
                      ;TEST whose initial value is 30 (decimal).
DEPTH DW − 200H   ;allocates a word (two bytes) to data labelled
                      ;DEPTH whose initial value is − 200 (hex).
VALUE DB 10H,20H,30H, − 30H,100H
                      ;allocates five bytes starting from a location labelled
                      ;VALUE. This is one method of entering a table in
                      ;the memory.
RESULT DW 10 DUP(?)
                      ;allocate 10 words (20 bytes) for a set of RESULTs,
                      ;each word initially containing an unknown value.
KEEP DW 10H,1AH,0A1H,0FFFFH,1FFFH,12 DUP (0)
                      ;allocate 17 words (34 bytes), the final twelve words
                      ;containing zero.

The last of these pseudo-ops highlights a point which must always be observed when writing assembly language programs, namely *precede any hex value in the range A to F, inclusive, with a 0*. That is, 1FFFH is an acceptable value, but FFFFH is not; the latter *must* be written in the form 0FFFFH.

A string of ASCII characters for use, say, as a message or table heading can be stored using the DB pseudo-op as follows:

MESSAGE   DB   'This is a message'

Additionally, an ASCII number (or series of numbers) can be stored as follows:

VAL_1   DB   '6','9','3','8'

SYMBOL DEFINITION PSEUDO-OPS

The EQU and ' = ' statements enable the programmer to assign a label or a name to an expression. For example

```
PORT_A              EQU 40H          ;PORT_A is given the value 40H
PORT_B              EQU PORT_A+2   ;PORT_B has the value 42H
FREEZING_POINT   EQU 0
```

SEGMENT DEFINITION PSEUDO-OPS

These enable the programmer to define the segments within the memory of the 8086 and 8088. The important directives are SEGMENT, ENDS and ASSUME. Each segment is 'opened' by means of a SEGMENT directive, and is terminated by an ENDS directive. The code segment must contain an ASSUME directive which tells the CPU what segment it must assume is referred to by each segment_label. The following illustrates one way in which the pseudo-ops are used to set up the stack segment, the data segment, the extra segment, and the code segment. Other examples are included in the programs later in the book.

```
MY_STACK   SEGMENT   PARA STACK     ;start of STACK segment
           DB        100H DUP(?)
MY_STACK   ENDS                      ;end of STACK segment
;***********************************
MY_DATA    SEGMENT                   ;start of DATA segment
ONE        DB        1H
TWO        DB        2H
THREE      DB        3H
MY_DATA    ENDS                      ;end of DATA segment
;***********************************
MY_EXTRA   SEGMENT                   ;start of EXTRA segment
TEST       DB        0FEH,0H,8H
RESULT     DB        5 DUP(?)
MY_EXTRA   ENDS                      ;end of EXTRA segment
;***********************************
```

```
MY_CODE    SEGMENT                              ;start of CODE segment
           ASSUME      SS:MY_STACK,DS:MY_DATA,ES:MY_EXTRA,
                       CS:MY_CODE
START:     MOV         AX,MY_DATA   ;initialize DATA segment
           MOV         DS,AX
           MOV         AX,MY_EXTRA  ;initialize EXTRA segment
           MOV         ES,AX
              .                     ;main program commences
              .
              .

MY_CODE    ENDS                                 ;end of CODE segment
           END         START                    ;end of assembly language program
```

Each segment *must* commence with a SEGMENT directive and end with an ENDS directive (END of Segment). The assembly language program finishes with an END directive, which is associated with a label, e.g., START, which tells the assembler what label is associated with the first instruction in the code segment. The SEGMENT directive may also be associated with another directive which tells the CPU how it is to organize the memory. For example, the PARA pseudo-op in MY_STACK tells the CPU to align the start of the stack segment with a PARAgraph in its memory, which is a 16-byte boundary in which the low-order four bits of the address are all zero.

The first instruction in the above program, labelled START, is one of the two instructions which initializes the DATA segment in the memory of the computer. You will recall from Fig. 3.1 that, initially, the DS and ES registers both point to the bottom of the PSP; we also mentioned earlier that the programmer must ensure that, during the program, the DS register points to the DATA segment and that the ES register points to the EXTRA segment. The two instructions

$$\text{MOV}\quad\text{AX,MY\_DATA}$$

$$\text{MOV}\quad\text{DS,AX}$$

make the DS register point to the start of the DATA segment in the memory of the computer, firstly by MOVing the 16-bit base address of the data segment into AX (remember, the ASSUME directive tells the CPU that MY_DATA is the label associated with the DATA segment) and secondly by MOVing the value in AX into the DS register.

In much the same way, the next two instructions in the program initialize the extra segment in the memory of the computer.

PROCEDURE DEFINITION PSEUDO-OPS

Procedures are 'named' subroutines (see Chapter 6 for full details), and a procedure can be 'called' into use from various places in the program. A procedure is defined by a PROC directive, and is terminated by an ENDP directive.

The procedure definition statement, PROC, should also indicate whether the procedure is a NEAR-type or FAR-type. That is, it should indicate whether the procedure is within the current code segment or is outside it; however, the NEAR attribute is not mandatory. Procedures are called into use by means of the CALL instruction, and the final instruction in the procedure is a RET (RETurn) instruction. This is illustrated in the following.

```
MY_CODE     SEGMENT                 ;start of CODE segment
            .                       ;initial instructions set up
            .                       ;code and extra segments, etc.
            .

;******************************
UPDATE      PROC    NEAR            ;UPDATE specified as a NEAR PROC
            ADD     AH,2            ;first instruction in procedure
            SUB     BH,3
            RET                     ;RETurn from procedure
UPDATE      ENDP                    ;END of Procedure
;******************************
START:      .                       ;first instruction in main program
            .

            CALL UPDATE             ;call procedure for first time
            .
            .

            CALL UPDATE             ;call procedure for second time
            .
            .

            HLT                     ;HaLT program
MY_CODE     ENDS                    ;end of code segment
            END     START           ;end of assembly program
```

The procedure UPDATE is declared as a NEAR procedure, so that any CALL which is made to it is assembled as an intrasegment CALL; any returns from it are assembled as intrasegment RETurns. There can, depending on the purpose of the procedure, be more than one RETurn to the calling program.

The final instruction in the main program is HLT (HaLT); this instruction puts the CPU in the 'halt' state, where it waits either for the RESET button on the CPU to be pressed, or for one of its interrupt pins to be activated (there can be more than one HLT instruction in the program).

TERMINATION PSEUDO-OPS

Each termination pseudo-op terminates a section of the program. You have already met the end-of-segment pseudo-op (ENDS) and the end-of-procedure pseudo-op (ENDP), each being paired with a 'beginning' statement such as SEGMENT and PROC, respectively. The END pseudo-op, which is the final statement in the program, differs from other termination psuedo-ops in that it does not have a 'beginning' statement. The form of the end statement is

$$\text{END} \quad \text{LABEL}$$

for example

$$\text{END} \quad \text{START}$$

where the label yields the 16-bit effective address of the first instruction to be executed. Examples of the END pseudo-op have been illustrated earlier in this section, and are to be found in programs later in the book.

EXTERNAL REFERENCE PSEUDO-OPS

These provide the programmer with the facility to use data in other programs and modules. The PUBLIC pseudo-op makes specified symbols available to other assembly modules that can be linked with the current module. The EXTRN pseudo-op identifies symbols which have been defined and declared public in some other assembly module. The INCLUDE pseudo-op merges an entire file of source statements into the current file at the time of assembly.

3.11   Instruction set summary

The instruction set of the CPU is a list of instructions which is available to the programmer. In this section, the instructions which are available to the 8088 user are briefly explained; you should refer to the appendix and to later chapters of the book for further details. The instructions are divided into six functional groups as follows:

A. Data transfer
B. Arithmetic
C. Bit manipulation
D. String manipulation
E. Control transfer
F. Processor control

A.   DATA TRANSFER INSTRUCTIONS

These instructions, listed in Table 3.2, are used to move bytes and words between memory and registers, and between the A-register and I/O ports.

B.   ARITHMETIC INSTRUCTIONS

These may be performed on four types of numbers, namely unsigned binary, signed binary, unsigned packed decimal, and unsigned unpacked decimal. The first three types are described in Chapter 4 and the last type in Chapter 10. The arithmetic instructions are summarized in Table 3.3.

Table 3.2 Data transfer instructions

General purpose	
MOV	Move a byte or word
PUSH	Push a word onto the stack
POP	Pop a word off the stack
XCHG	Exchange byte or word
XLAT	Translate byte
Input/output	
IN	Input byte or word
OUT	Output byte or word
Address object	
LEA	Load effective address
LDS	Load pointer using DS register
LES	Load point using ES register
Flag transfer	
LAHF	Load AH register from flags register
SAHF	Save AH register in the flags register
PUSHF	Push the flags register onto the stack
POPF	Pop the flags register off the stack

Table 3.3 Arithmetic instructions

Addition	
ADD	Add byte or word
ADC	Add byte or word with carry
INC	Increment byte or word by unity
AAA	ASCII adjust for addition
DAA	Decimal adjust for addition
Subtraction	
SUB	Subtract byte or word
SBB	Subtract byte or word with borrow
DEC	Decrement byte or word by unity
NEG	Negate byte or word (negative value)
CMP	Compare byte or word
AAS	ASCII adjust for subtraction
DAS	Decimal adjust for subtraction
Multiplication	
MUL	Multiply byte or word (unsigned)
IMUL	Integer multiply byte or word
AAM	ASCII adjust for multiplication
Division	
DIV	Divide byte or word (unsigned)
IDIV	Integer divide byte or word
AAD	ASCII adjust for division
CBW	Convert byte to word
CWD	Convert word to doubleword

Table 3.4   Bit, byte and word manipulation instructions

Logical	
NOT	NOT byte or word
AND	AND byte or word
OR	Inclusive OR byte or word
XOR	EXCLUSIVE OR byte or word
TEST	TEST byte or word
Shift	
SHL/SAL	Shift logical/arithmetic left byte or word
SHR	Shift logical right byte or word
SAR	Shift arithmetic right byte or word
Rotate	
ROL	Rotate left byte or word
ROR	Rotate right byte or word
RCL	Rotate through carry left byte or word
RCR	Rotate through carry right byte or word

Table 3.5   String instructions

REP	Repeat
REPE/REPZ	Repeat while equal/zero
REPNE/REPNZ	Repeat while not equal/not zero
MOVS/MOVSB/MOVSW	Move byte or word string
COMPS	Compare byte or word string
SCAS	Scan byte or word string
LODS	Load byte or word string
STOS	Store byte or word string

C. BIT, BYTE AND WORD MANIPULATION INSTRUCTIONS

These are used to manipulate bits which are in bytes or words either by means of logical instructions, or by 'shift' instructions, or by 'rotate' instructions. The bit manipulation instructions are summarized in Table 3.4, the logical instructions are described in Chapter 4, and the shift and rotate instructions are included in Chapter 5.

D. STRING INSTRUCTIONS

The string instructions, or *string primitives*, operate on strings in the form of a sequence of bytes or of words (see Chapter 10 for details); the length of a string may be up to 128 Kbytes. The instructions (see Table 3.5) can move strings, compare strings, or scan strings. A range of 'repeat' instructions can be used with the string instructions, allowing the computer to repeat a specific string instruction until a certain condition is reached (these are also listed in Table 3.5).

Table 3.6 shows how the string instructions use the flags and registers of the CPU.

Table 3.6   Register and flag use by string instructions

SI	Index (offset) for source string
DI	Index (offset) for destination string
CX	Repetition counter
AL/AX	Scan value for SCAS / Destination for LODS / Source for STOS
DF	0 = auto-increment SI and DI / 1 = auto-decrement SI and DI
ZF	Scan/compare terminator

Table 3.7   Program control transfer instructions

Unconditional transfers	
CALL	Call procedure
RET	Return from procedure
JMP	Jump
Conditional transfers	
JA/JNBE	Jump if above/not below or equal
JAE/JNB/JNC	Jump if above or equal/not below/no carry
JB/JNAE/JC	Jump if below/not above or equal/carry
JBE/JNA	Jump if below or equal/not above
JE/JZ	Jump if equal/zero
JG/JNLE	Jump if greater/not less or equal
JGE/JNL	Jump if greater or equal/not less
JL/JNGE	Jump if less/not greater or equal
JLE/JNG	Jump if less or equal/not greater
JNE/JNZ	Jump if not equal/not zero
JNO	Jump if no overflow
JNP/JPO	Jump if not parity/parity odd
JNS	Jump if not sign
JO	Jump if overflow
JP/JPE	Jump if parity/parity even
JS	Jump if sign
Iteration controls	
LOOP	Loop
LOOPE/LOOPZ	Loop if equal/zero
LOOPNE/LOOPNZ	Loop if not equal/not zero
JCXZ	Jump if CX = 0
Interrupt	
INT	Interrupt
INTO	Interrupt if overflow
IRET	Interrupt return

Table 3.8   Processor control instructions

Flag operations	
STC	Set carry flag
CLC	Clear carry flag
CMC	Complement carry flag
STD	Set direction flag
CLD	Clear direction flag
STI	Set interrupt enable flag
CLI	Clear interrupt enable flag
External synchronization	
HLT	Halt until interrupt or reset
WAIT	Wait for $\overline{\text{TEST}}$ pin active
ESC	Escape to external processor
LOCK	Lock bus during next instruction
No operation	
NOP	No operation

E.   CONTROL TRANSFER INSTRUCTIONS

Occasionally it is necessary to transfer control from an instruction in the program to another instruction which is not in sequence. These instructions are the control transfer instructions, and are described in Chapter 5. There are four broad categories of this type of instruction, which are listed in Table 3.7.

An unconditional transfer or 'jump' instruction is one which causes a transfer of control to occur unconditionally, and has no regard for any other event in the program.

A conditional jump is one which occurs when a particular condition has been tested (for example, a test can be made to see if the ZF has been set) and, if the test is satisfied, the jump or transfer is made. If the result is not satisfied, the CPU ignores the 'jump if' command and processes the next instruction in sequence. A conditional jump may only be made to an instruction which is within ±128 bytes of the conditional jump instruction.

Iteration control instructions are used to regulate software loops. These instructions use the CX register as a 'loop counter' and, as with conditional jumps, they can only be made within ±128 bytes of the LOOP instruction.

Interrupt instructions allow the program to be interrupted at any point, but only when the instruction currently being executed is complete. Details of interrupt operation are given in Chapter 9.

F.   PROCESSOR CONTROL INSTRUCTIONS

These instructions (see Table 3.8) enable various CPU activities to be controlled by program instructions. The flag operation instructions allow certain flags to be set or cleared; the external synchronization instructions allow the CPU to be synchronized with events which are external to the CPU. Finally, the NOP

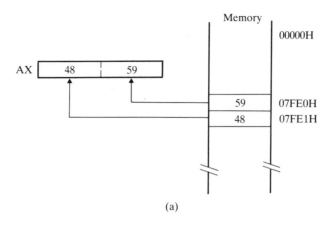

(a)

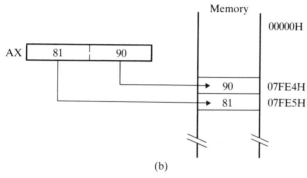

(b)

Figure 3.4   Moving 16 bits of data (a) from the memory to register AX, (b) from register AX to the memory.

instruction is a No OPeration or 'do nothing' command; the NOP instruction is often inserted in a program where it is expected that, at a later time, an instruction will be needed. Alternatively, the NOP instruction can be used as a time wasting instruction which trims a timing program to give a more accurate timing period.

3.12   Moving 16 bits of data between a register and a memory

Data is moved in the 8088 in a byte-wise fashion, so that eight bits at a time are moved between a register and a memory (even if the register is 16 bits 'wide'). The way in which the move is organized is shown in Fig. 3.4.

Figure 3.4(a) shows how 16 bits of data, stored in byte form in the memory locations at addresses 07FE0 and 07FE1, are moved into register AX. Firstly, the data at the lowest memory address is moved into the low byte of the register and, secondly, the byte at the higher address is moved into the low byte of the register.

When moving data from a 16-bit register to the memory (see Fig. 3.4(b)), the data in the low byte of the register is moved to the lowest address in the memory, following which the data in the high byte of the register is moved into the next higher address in the memory.

4
Arithmetic and logic

4.1 Arithmetic instructions in the 8086 and 8088

The arithmetic instructions which are available in the 8086 and 8088 instruction set include addition, subtraction, multiplication, division, incrementing, decrementing and comparison.

The programs included in this chapter are intended to illustrate the general principles involved in their use.

4.2 An 8-bit addition and subtraction program

Since this is the first practical program we will discuss, it will be studied in some detail; programs written thereafter receive less detailed treatment.

Initially you type in Listing 4.1 using the EDLIN utility of the computer; when entering EDLIN you should call the program 41.ASM (if you call it 4.1.ASM, the computer gets confused by the two 'dots' in the file name). Program lines 1, 2, 6 and 14 commence with a semicolon (;); the CPU interprets the whole of these lines as comments which are not part of the program itself. Similarly, many lines after line 16 also contain comments which the CPU ignores. As mentioned in Chapter 3, comments are included to make the program more readable.

A *stack*, which is an area of memory set aside for a special purpose (see Chapter 6 for details), is initialized in program line 3, and is closed in line 5. The information in line 4 tells the computer that the stack is to be 100H (256) bytes long, and that it can initially be filled with electronic 'garbage' (symbolized by the DUP(?) command).

The *data segment* is an area of memory which stores data for the program; the segment is initialized in line 7 and is terminated in line 13. The length of the data segment used is five bytes (the fact that bytes rather than words are specified is indicated by DB in lines 8–12, inclusive). The first three items stored in the data

```
 1: ;****LISTING 4.1 - 8-BIT ADD, SUBTRACT, DECREMENT AND INCREMENT****
 2: ;****STACK SEGMENT****
 3: MY_STACK          SEGMENT PARA          STACK
 4:          DB       100H    DUP(?)
 5: MY_STACK          ENDS
 6: ;****DATA SEGMENT****
 7: MY_DATA  SEGMENT
 8: VAL_1    DB       49H
 9: VAL_2    DB       52H
10: VAL_3    DB       80H
11: SUM      DB       (?)
12: DIFF     DB       (?)
13: MY_DATA ENDS
14: ;****CODE SEGMENT****
15: MY_CODE SEGMENT
16: ASSUME   CS:MY_CODE,DS:MY_DATA,SS:MY_STACK
17: START:   MOV      AX,MY_DATA      ;TWO INSTRUCTIONS TO INITIALIZE
18:          MOV      DS,AX           ;DATA SEGMENT (DS)
19:          MOV      BX,0108H        ;LOAD BH AND BL WITH DATA
20:          SUB      AX,AX           ;CLEAR (AX)
21:          MOV      AL,VAL_1        ;FETCH AUGEND
22:          ADD      AL,VAL_2        ;ADD 1st ADDEND
23:          ADD      AL,50H          ;ADD A CONSTANT
24:          MOV      SUM,AL          ;STORE SUM
25:          SUB      AL,VAL_3        ;SUBTRACT SUBTRAHEND
26:          NOP                      ;FOR FUTURE USE
27:          MOV      DIFF,AL         ;STORE DIFFERENCE
28:          DEC      BL              ;DECREMENT BL
29:          DEC      BL
30:          DEC      BL
31:          INC      BH
32:          INC      BH
33:          INC      BH              ;INCREMENT BH
34:          INT      23H             ;RETURN CONTROL TO KEYBOARD
35: MY_CODE  ENDS                     ;END OF CODE SEGMENT
36: END      START                    ;END OF PROGRAM
```

segment are called VAL_1, VAL_2 and VAL_3, having the values 49H, 52H and 80H, respectively. The final two bytes in the segment contain items called SUM and DIFF, corresponding to the sum and difference of numbers in the program. Since we do not know the values of SUM and DIFF at this stage, they are initially allowed to contain garbage.

The *code segment* starts in line 15; this is the segment in which the program itself resides. Line 16 tells the CPU the names it must ASSUME that represent the code segment (CS), the data segment (DS) and the stack segment (SS), respectively. The first instruction in the program (see line 17) must be preceded by a label designating the commencement of the program; we use the label START for this purpose. The instructions in lines 17 and 18 establish the address of the data segment by loading the 16-bit segment base address into the data segment register (DS) via register AX. It may be the case that some programs you write do not have a data segment; in this case, the instructions in lines 17 and 18 are not necessary, and the DS:MY_DATA statement in line 16 would be omitted.

The program really gets to work in line 19 by loading data into registers BH (01H is put into this register) and BL (08H is put in this). In line 20, the program empties or clears out the contents of register AX. There are several methods of doing this, one being by subtracting the contents of AX from itself, as shown in line 20. The mnemonic for the subtract instruction is

SUB destination,source

where the 'source' is the source of the data, which may either be a register (as it is here), or a memory location, or a number. The function of the SUBtract instruction is

destination = destination − source

That is, the instruction subtracts the source data from the destination data, leaving the result in the destination. Consequently, the SUB AX,AX instruction subtracts the contents of register AX from the contents of register AX, leaving the result (zero) in register AX. Other instructions which can be used to clear the contents of register AX are

MOV AX,0H

and

XOR AX,AX

The MOVe instruction above represents the operation

MOV destination,source

This instruction MOVes a copy of the contents of the source data into the destination. Hence, the instruction MOV AX,0H causes zero to be moved into register AX.

The XOR instruction is a 'logical' instruction, and discussion is deferred to a later point in the chapter.

In line 21, VAL_1 (49H) is MOVed in the 8-bit AL register and in line 22 the value VAL_2 is added to it. The mnemonic for the addition instruction is

$$ADD \quad destination,source$$

The source may be the contents of a register, or of a memory location (as it is in this case since the data is stored in the data segment, i.e., in the memory), or it may simply be a number. The instruction may manipulate either a byte or a word, and the function performed is

$$destination = destination + source$$

You should note that the ADD instruction takes no regard of the content of the carry flag; when handling very long numbers (see Listing 4.5), you will need to use the ADC instruction (ADd with Carry) to deal with the carry passes between bytes (or words). Thus, when the instruction in line 22 has been executed, register AL contains the sum of VAL_1 and VAL_2.

The ADD AL,50H instruction in line 23 simply adds 50H to the value in register AL; this illustrates how a constant can be added.

Next, the value in the AL register is saved in the location SUM reserved for it in the data sector; the instruction MOV SUM,AL does this for you. You, of course, do not know the address of SUM, but it is a relatively simple matter to determine its address by examining the data sector after you have run the program.

In line 25, the value VAL_3 (80H) is subtracted from the contents of AL by the SUB AL,VAL_3 instruction. The mnemonic of the subtract instruction is written as follows:

$$SUB \quad destination,source$$

where the source of the data may either be a register, or a memory location, or it may be a number. The function performed is

$$destination = destination - source$$

That is, SUB AL,VAL_3 subtracts VAL_3 from the contents of AL, leaving the difference in AL. The NOP instruction in line 26 is a No OPeration instruction, which causes the CPU to do nothing. This instruction is used here simply to leave room in the program for a later modification.

Next, the MOV DIFF,AL instruction in line 27 transfers a copy of the difference produced by the instruction in line 25 to the location DIFF reserved for it in the DATA segment.

The final few lines of the program illustrate the operation of the DECrement and INCrement instructions. The instruction in line 19 of the program loaded 01H into register BH and 08H in BL. Lines 28, 29 and 30 contain a DECrement

(DEC) instruction whose mnemonic is

DEC destination

which carries out the function

destination = destination − 1

That is, the instruction DEC BL has the effect of reducing or decrementing the contents of BL by unity, leaving the reduced value in BL. At the end of the three decrement instructions, BL contains $8 − 3 = 5H$.

Next there follows three INCrement (INC) instructions whose mnemonic is

INC destination

and whose function is

destination = destination + 1

That is, the instruction INC BH increments the contents of BH by unity, leaving the incremented value in BH. At the end of the three INC instructions, BH contains $1 + 3 = 4H$.

INC and DEC instructions are frequently used as part of a counting sequence, in which the value stored in a register or memory (the 'counter') is either incremented or decremented until a specific value is reached. In most cases a positive 'counter' value is used, and it is decremented until it reaches zero; the state of the counter is tested after each decrementing process. This technique is used in many programs in this book.

The INT 23H instruction in line 34 terminates the program by generating an 'internal' INTerrupt signal (see Chapter 9 for details), which returns control to the keyboard. (*Note:* the interrupt type number may differ between different makes of computer); this results in the VDU displaying a prompt signal indicating that the keyboard is waiting for instructions.

Alternative methods of terminating the program are available and two are described below. One is to replace line 34 with the following:

34: STOP: JMP STOP   ;INFINITE LOOP

As soon as the above version of line 34 is executed, program control is returned to line 34 once more, i.e., it JuMPs (JMP) to the label STOP. This causes the computer to enter an infinite loop, from which you can escape by pressing the RESET button on the computer; the net result is, of course, that you must re-enter the system. Another alternative is to use the HALT instruction as follows:

34:        HLT   ;ENTER THE HALT STATE

An escape is made from the half state either by pressing the RESET button (see above), or by applying an interrupt signal to the CPU (see Chapter 9).

Table 4.1 The '.LST' listing of Program 4.1

```
 1                                    ;****LISTING 4.1 – 8-BIT, ADD, SUBTRACT,
                                           DECREMENT AND INCREMENT****
 2                                    ;****STACK SEGMENT****
 3  0000                             MY_STACK    SEGMENT PARA    STACK
 4  0000  0100[                                  DB      100H    DUP (?)
 5              ??
 6            ]
 7
 8  0100                             MY_STACK    ENDS
 9                                    ;****DATA SEGMENT****
10  0000                             MY_DATA SEGMENT
11  0000  49                         VAL_1   DB      49H
12  0001  52                         VAL_2   DB      52H
13  0002  80                         VAL_3   DB      80H
14  0003  ??                         SUM     DB      (?)
15  0004  ??                         DIFF    DB      (?)
16  0005                             MY_DATA ENDS
17                                    ;****CODE SEGMENT****
18  0000                             MY_CODE SEGMENT
19                                              ASSUME  CS:MY_CODE,DS:MY_DATA,SS:MY_STACK
20  0000  B8 ---- R          START:   MOV     AX,MY_DATA    ;TWO INSTRUCTIONS TO INITIALIZE
21  0003  8E D8                       MOV     DS,AX         ;DATA SEGMENT (DS)
22  0005  BB 0108                     MOV     BX,0108H      ;LOAD BH AND BL WITH DATA
23  0008  2B C0                       SUB     AX,AX         ;CLEAR(AX)
24  000A  A0 0000 R                   MOV     AL,VAL_1      ;FETCH AUGEND
25  000D  02 06 0001 R                ADD     AL,VAL_2      ;ADD 1st ADDEND
26  0011  04 50                       ADD     AL,50H        ;ADD A CONSTANT
27  0013  A2 0003 R                   MOV     SUM,AL        ;STORE SUM
28  0016  2A 06 0002 R                SUB     AL,VAL_3      ;SUBTRACT SUBTRAHEND
29  001A  90                          NOP                   ;FOR FUTURE USE
30  001B  A2 0004 R                   MOV     DIFF,AL       ;STORE DIFFERENCE
31  001E  FE CB                       DEC     BL            ;DECREMENT BL
```

Table 4.1 Continued

```
32  0020  FE  CB      DEC  BL
33  0022  FE  CB      DEC  BL
34  0024  FE  C7      INC  BH
35  0026  FE  C7      INC  BH
36  0028  FE  C7      INC  BH       ;INCREMENT BH
37  002A  CD  23      INT  23H      ;RETURN CONTROL TO KEYBOARD
38  002C            MY_CODE ENDS    ;END OF CODE SEGMENT
39                   END  START     ;END OF PROGRAM
```

Segments and groups:

Name	Size	align	combine class
MY_CODE	002C	PARA	NONE
MY_DATA	0005	PARA	NONE
MY_STACK	0100	PARA	STACK

Symbols:

Name	Type	Value	Attr.
DIFF	L BYTE	0004	MY_DATA
START	L NEAR	0000	MY_CODE
SUM	L BYTE	0003	MY_DATA
VAL_1	L BYTE	0000	MY_DATA
VAL_2	L BYTE	0001	MY_DATA
VAL_3	L BYTE	0002	MY_DATA

```
Warning   Severe
Errors    Errors
0         0
```

You are warned at this point that, although JMP STOP instruction and the HLT instruction do prevent the program from proceeding further, they also leave the computer in an electronic 'black hole'. That is, the program is held up pending the reset button being pressed (or an interrupt occurring), but they cause the cursor to vanish from the screen! These methods are not generally advised unless they offer some advantage.

Line 35 ends the code segment, and the END instruction in line 36 terminates the program; the 'START' label in line 36 tells the assembler program where to begin assembling the program.

4.3 The '.LST' listing of the program

As outlined in Chapter 3, you can produce several files during the assembly and linking phases, and perhaps one of the most useful of them is the '.LST' file. This provides not only an assembly listing of the program, but also a machine code (hex) listing. Perhaps more importantly it gives a print-out of any errors in the program at the point at which they are detected. Since this listing contains more data than the '.ASM' file, it also takes up a larger storage area on the disk. The '.LST' file for the program in Listing 4.1 is given in Table 4.1.

The left-hand column of numbers in the '.LST' file corresponds to the printed line number for each line of the '.LST' file. You are warned at this point that these line numbers do not generally agree with the line numbers associated with the '.ASM' file listing (see Listing 4.1).

Next to this are a range of hex values representing the 16-bit offsets relative to the start of the various segments in the memory. Thus, the address 0000 in lines 3 and 4 of '.LST' is the first address in the stack segment; the address 0000 in lines 10 and 11 is the first address in the data segment, and the 0000 in lines 18 and 20 refer to the code segment.

The values printed in the next column of the data segment (see lines 11–15, inclusive, of '.LST') are the hex values of VAL_1, VAL_2, VAL_3, SUM and DIFF (although the latter two are designated the value ?? at the time of producing '.LST'). The numbers printed next to the offsets in the code segment (see lines 20 to 37, inclusive, of '.LST') are the hex machine code representation of the assembly language program. Where 'R' is printed in this section, the CPU must reference one of the segment registers in order to determine the actual address. Finally, the '.LST' listing provides information about the segments, groups and symbols.

4.4 Single-step running the program

The DEBUG utility provides a routine for single-stepping through the program. Table 4.2 shows the print-out at each step or 'breakpoint' for the add/subtract program in Listing 4.1. At each breakpoint the state of the registers and flags is interrogated by the CPU.

Table 4.2 Print-out step by step

```
>T
AX=07FF  BX=0000  CX=0035  DX=0000  SP=0100  BP=0000  SI=0000     DI=0000
DS=07EC  ES=07EC  SS=0800  CS=07FC  IP=0003     NV UP DI PL NZ NA PO NC
07FC:0003 8ED8        MOV   DS,AX
>T
AX=07FF  BX=0108  CX=0035  DX=0000  SP=0100  BP=0000  SI=0000     DI=0000
DS=07FF  ES=07EC  SS=0800  CS=07FC  IP=0008     NV UP DI PL NZ NA PO NC
07FC:0008 2BC0        SUB   AX,AX
>T
AX=0000  BX=0108  CX=0035  DX=0000  SP=0100  BP=0000  SI=0000     DI=0000
DS=07FF  ES=07EC  SS=0800  CS=07FC  IP=000A     NV UP DI PL ZR NA PE NC
07FC:000A A00000      MOV   AL,[0000]                             DS:0000=49
>T
AX=0049  BX=0108  CX=0035  DX=0000  SP=0100  BP=0000  SI=0000     DI=0000
DS=07FF  ES=07EC  SS=0800  CS=07FC  IP=000D     NV UP DI PL ZR NA PE NC
07FC:000D 02060100    ADD   AL,[0001]                             DS:0001=52
>T
AX=009B  BX=0108  CX=0035  DX=0000  SP=0100  BP=0000  SI=0000     DI=0000
DS=07FF  ES=07EC  SS=0800  CS=07FC  IP=0011     OV UP DI NG NZ NA PO NC
07FC:0011 0450        ADD   AL,50
>T
AX=00EB  BX=0108  CX=0035  DX=0000  SP=0100  BP=0000  SI=0000     DI=0000
DS=07FF  ES=07EC  SS=0800  CS=07FC  IP=0013     NV UP DI NG NZ NA PE NC
07FC:0013 A20300      MOV   [0003],AL                             DS:0003=00
>T
AX=00EB  BX=0108  CX=0035  DX=0000  SP=0100  BP=0000  SI=0000     DI=0000
DS=07FF  ES=07EC  SS=0800  CS=07FC  IP=0016     NV UP DI NG NZ NA PE NC
07FC:0016 2A060200    SUB   AL,[0002]                             DS:0002=80
>T
```

Table 4.2 Continued

```
AX=006B  BX=0108  CX=0035  DX=0000  SP=0100  BP=0000  SI=0000  DI=0000
DS=07FF  ES=07EC  SS=0800  CS=07FC  IP=001A  NV UP DI PL NZ NA PO NC
07FC:001A 90          NOP
>T

AX=006B  BX=0108  CX=0035  DX=0000  SP=0100  BP=0000  SI=0000  DI=0000
DS=07FF  ES=07EC  SS=0800  CS=07FC  IP=001B  NV UP DI PL NZ NA PO NC
07FC:001B A20400      MOV     [0004],AL                      DS:0004=00
>T

AX=006B  BX=0108  CX=0035  DX=0000  SP=0100  BP=0000  SI=0000  DI=0000
DS=07FF  ES=07EC  SS=0800  CS=07FC  IP=001E  NV UP DI PL NZ NA PO NC
07FC:001E FECB        DEC     BL
>T

AX=006B  BX=0107  CX=0035  DX=0000  SP=0100  BP=0000  SI=0000  DI=0000
DS=07FF  ES=07EC  SS=0800  CS=07FC  IP=0020  NV UP DI PL NZ NA PO NC
07FC:0020 FECB        DEC     BL
>T

AX=006B  BX=0106  CX=0035  DX=0000  SP=0100  BP=0000  SI=0000  DI=0000
DS=07FF  ES=07EC  SS=0800  CS=07FC  IP=0022  NV UP DI PL NZ NA PE NC
07FC:0022 FECB        DEC     BL
>T

AX=006B  BX=0105  CX=0035  DX=0000  SP=0100  BP=0000  SI=0000  DI=0000
DS=07FF  ES=07EC  SS=0800  CS=07FC  IP=0024  NV UP DI PL NZ NA PE NC
07FC:0024 FEC7        INC     BH
>T

AX=006B  BX=0205  CX=0035  DX=0000  SP=0100  BP=0000  SI=0000  DI=0000
DS=07FF  ES=07EC  SS=0800  CS=07FC  IP=0026  NV UP DI PL NZ NA PO NC
07FC:0026 FEC7        INC     BH
>T
```

Table 4.2 Continued

```
AX=006B  BX=0305  CX=0035  DX=0000  SP=0100  BP=0000  SI=0000  DI=0000
DS=07FF  ES=07EC  SS=0800  CS=07FC  IP=0028  NV UP DI PL NZ NA PE NC
07FC:0028 FEC7  INC  BH
>T

AX=006B  BX=0405  CX=0035  DX=0000  SP=0100  BP=0000  SI=0000  DI=0000
DS=07FF  ES=07EC  SS=0800  CS=07FC  IP=002A  NV UP DI PL NZ NA PO NC
07FC:002A CD23  INT  23
>T

AX=006B  BX=0405  CX=0035  DX=0000  SP=00FA  BP=0000  SI=0000  DI=0000
DS=07FF  ES=07EC  SS=0800  CS=063E  IP=080D  NV UP DI PL NZ NA PO NC
063E:080D 83C406  ADD  SP,+06
```

Some points to note about Table 4.2 are as follows. The first line printed out at each breakpoint contains the 16-bit contents of the registers in the EU, and the second line contains the 16-bit contents of registers in the BIU together with the state of eight of the flags.

The third line contains information relating to the current state of the program. To illustrate the meaning of the third line, we will consider a typical example. The data in the third line of the sixth block of data in Table 4.2 is as follows:

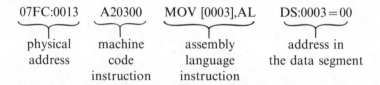

The left-most item of data combines the 16-bit content of the CS register with the 16-bit content of the IP, and enables you to determine the 20-bit physical address of the instruction which is about to be executed. This address is

$$[07FCH \times 10H] + 0013H = 07FC0 + 0013 = 07FD3H$$

The machine code version of the instruction which is about to be executed is three bytes in length, the three bytes being given by the block of data A20300. That is, A2 is stored in location 07FD3H, 03 is stored in location 07FD4H, and 00 is stored in location 07FD5H.

The assembly language instruction which is about to be executed is printed next, and is given as MOV [0003],AL. This differs from the instruction entered into the source file (which was MOV SUM,AL). You will notice that in the '.LST' listing of the program, the memory location SUM was given the 'value' 0003 within the MY_DATA segment; that is, the effective address of 'SUM' is 0003 within the DATA segment. The CPU therefore interprets the source code instruction MOV SUM,AL as MOV [0003],AL.

The information at the right-hand end of the third line of the block gives the data that is currently in location 'SUM' within the data segment. The information is printed in the form

$$DS:0003 = 00$$

That is, the value 00H which is initially in location 'SUM' is electronic 'garbage'.

After the MOV [0003],AL instruction has been executed (see the 7th breakpoint), the value in AL (which is EBH) has been stored in SUM. You will also note that the value in the IP has increased from 0013 by 3 (which is equal to the number of bytes in the MOV SUM,AL instruction in breakpoint 6) to 0016 (this is reflected in the data at the left-hand side of the third line at breakpoint 7).

Table 4.3 A typical print-out of results

	49	52	80	EB	6B	FF	02	FD-02	FF	02	FD	02	FF	02	FD	IR.kk..}..}..}
07FF:0000	00	00	00	00	00	00	00	00→00	00	00	00	00	00	00	00	....
07FF:0010	00	00	00	00	00	00	00	00→00	00	00	00	00	00	00	00	....
07FF:0020	00	00	00	00	00	00	00	00→00	00	00	00	00	00	00	00	....
07FF:0030	00	00	00	00	00	00	00	00→00	00	00	00	00	00	00	00	....
07FF:0040	00	00	00	00	00	00	00	00→00	00	00	00	00	00	00	00	....
07FF:0050	00	00	00	00	00	00	00	00→00	00	00	00	00	00	00	00	....
07FF:0060	00	00	00	00	00	00	00	00→00	00	00	00	00	00	00	00	....
07FF:0070	00	00	00	00	00	00	00	00→00	00	00	00	00	00	00	00	....

4.5   Displaying the results

The values VAL_1, VAL_2 and VAL_3 together with the results (SUM and DIFF) are contained in the data segment. Whilst still in the DEBUG utility, you can examine the results after a complete run of the program by typing DDS:0 followed by return. This displays the first 128 bytes of the data segment on the screen, a typical print-out being shown in Table 4.3.

Each line of the display corresponds to sixteen bytes of data in two groups of eight bytes separated by a hyphen. The ASCII version of the information on the line is printed on the extreme right of the data line. The data segment simply comprises the first five bytes (see also the information provided by the 'Segments and groups' section of Table 4.1). The values in this segment are 49, 52, 80, EB and 6B; the first three correspond to VAL_1, VAL_2 and VAL_3, and the final two to SUM and DIFF (you should check these values against the calculation in the program).

4.6   Decimal addition and subtraction

The basis of decimal addition using packed BCD arithmetic was outlined in Chapter 1. From this you will appreciate that, in order to perform decimal arithmetic, it is simply a matter of *entering the data in hex* and decimal adjusting the result *after* each addition or subtraction. The decimal adjustment instructions used for addition and subtraction are, respectively

DAA   ;DECIMAL ADJUST ADDITION

DAS   ;DECIMAL ADJUST SUBTRACTION

Listing 4.1 can easily be amended to handle decimal arithmetic as follows. Firstly, copy the file 41.ASM (corresponding to the '.ASM' version of Listing 4.1) into another file called 42.ASM, and amend certain lines in this file as shown in Listing 4.2. You will note that the value of VAL_2 is reduced to 42 to ensure that the decimal sum is not too large for the destination location (which is 8 bits 'wide', and can only handle a decimal number which is in the range 0–99). You will also notice that the 'decimal' data is input to the program in lines 8, 9 and 10 as hex data. The reason for this is that, should you input the data as a decimal value, the computer would convert it to hex, giving the wrong result! For example, if you wrote in line 8 that VAL_1 = 49, the computer would store it as the hex value 31, which is not the value required. Having initially included the 'decimal' values as hex, the DAA (or DAS) instruction converts the sum (or the difference) into the correct decimal value at a later stage.

As before, line 22 of the program adds VAL_1 to VAL_2 in hex (to give a sum of 8BH) and, in line 23 of Listing 4.2, the sum is 'adjusted' to the correct packed BCD form (91) by the DAA instruction.

```
 1: ;****LISTING 4.2 – DECIMAL ADD AND SUBTRACT****
 8: VAL_1        DB          49H
 9: VAL_2        DB          42H
10: VAL_3        DB          39H
11: SUM          DB          (?)
12: DIFF         DB          (?)
23:              DAA                     ;DECIMAL ADJUST ADDITION
26:              DAS                     ;DECIMAL ADJUST SUBTRACTION
28:              NOP
29:              NOP
30:              NOP
31:              NOP
32:              NOP
33:              NOP
```

Similarly, line 25 of the program subtracts VAL_3 (= 39) from the SUM to give a hex difference of 58; the DAS instruction adjusts this to the packed BCD (decimal) value of 52.

Since we have already studied the effect of the DEC and INC instructions, lines 28–33, inclusive, of the original program are replaced by NOPs. The five bytes in the data segment after the program has run are therefore

$$49 \quad 42 \quad 39 \quad 91 \quad 52$$

which respectively represent VAL_1, VAL_2, VAL_3, SUM and DIFF.

4.7   ASCII addition and subtraction

As outlined in Chapter 1, the computer may receive numerical data in the ASCII code, which is a form of unpacked BCD (see Appendix B for the ASCII code). The decimal numbers 0–9 are transmitted in ASCII as the hex numbers 30–39, respectively; that is, the most significant four bits of the data byte are not relevant in any mathematical operation.

The CPU handles ASCII addition by adding (or subtracting) the ASCII values in their hex form; the result is then converted into its correct value either by using an AAA instruction (ASCII Adjust Addition) or an AAS instruction (ASCII Adjust Subtraction). This process is illustrated in Listing 4.3; the lines in this listing are merely the lines which need editing in Listing 4.2.

In lines 8–10, inclusive, the values VAL_1, VAL_2 and VAL_3 are entered as ASCII values by enclosing them in single quotes; that is, they are stored in the data segment as the hex values 35, 34 and 36, respectively. As before, program line 22 adds VAL_2 to VAL_1 in hex, leaving the result (69) in AL. The AAA instruction in line 23 strips off the most significant nibble, leaving 09 in AL, which is stored by line 24 in the location SUM.

The subtraction instruction in line 25 subtracts VAL_3 from SUM to give 09H − 36H = D3H in AL. The AAS instruction in line 26 leaves the correct

```
 1: ;****LISTING 4.3 – ASCII ADD AND SUBTRACT****
 8: VAL_1       DB          '5'
 9: VAL_2       DB          '4'
10: VAL_3       DB          '6'
11: SUM         DB          (?)
12: DIFF        DB          (?)
23:             AAA                     ;ASCII ADJUST FOR ADDITION
26:             AAS                     ;ASCII ADJUST FOR SUBTRACTION
```

decimal value of 03 in AL; line 27 of the program stores this value in location DIFF.

At the end of the program, the data segment contains the values

$$35 \quad 34 \quad 36 \quad 09 \quad 03$$

corresponding to the ASCII values 5, 4 and 6, together with SUM = 9 and DIFF = 3.

4.8   16-bit addition and subtraction

16-bit addition can be handled directly by the 8086 and 8088 CPUs, as illustrated in Listing 4.4 (which is a modification of Listing 4.1). Lines 8–10, inclusive, specify three 16-bit values to be used in the program, and lines 11 and 12 reserve two 16-bit locations in the memory for the SUM and DIFFerence produced by the program.

As with the 8-bit addition, program lines 21 and 22 add the 16-bit values VAL_1 and VAL_2 together to give the following in register AX:

$$4859H + 5162H = 99BBH$$

Line 23 adds a further 5050H to this value, after which AX contains EA0BH. This value is stored in the 16-bit memory location SUM by program line 24.

Next, VAL_3 (8190H) is subtracted from SUM to leave 687BH in AX, which is stored in location DIFF. A print-out of the ten bytes of the data sector after

```
 1: ;****LISTING 4.4 – 16-BIT ADD AND SUBTRACT****
 8: VAL_1       DW          4859H
 9: VAL_2       DW          5162H
10: VAL_3       DW          8190H
11: SUM         DW          (?)
12: DIFF        DW          (?)
21:             MOV         AX,VAL_1        ;FETCH AUGEND
22:             ADD         AX,VAL_2        ;ADD 1st ADDEND
23:             ADD         AX,5050H        ;ADD A CONSTANT
24:             MOV         SUM,AX          ;STORE SUM
25:             SUB         AX,VAL_3        ;SUBTRACT SUBTRAHEND
26:             NOP
27:             MOV         DIFF,AX         ;STORE DIFFERENCE
```

the program has run is as follows:

59   48   62   51   90   81   0B   EA   7B   68

As mentioned in Chapter 3, the 8088 stores values in memory in a byte-by-byte basis, the low byte being stored first. Hence, the 16-bit VAL_1 (4859H) is stored in the first two bytes of the data segment as 59   48; VAL_2 (5162H) is stored as 62   51, etc. The SUM (EA0BH) is stored as 0B   EA, and DIFF (687BH) is stored as 7B   68.

4.9   Multi-byte addition and subtraction

When addition or subtraction is performed in practice, we often need either to add or to subtract very long numbers. The addition and subtraction programs referred to earlier deal with only either a simple 8-bit or a 16-bit addition, and do not account for any 'carry' which may occur between bytes in a multi-byte addition (or a 'borrow' which may occur in a multibyte subtraction), nor for a carry which is produced by the addition of the most significant bytes.

In this section we look at a program which not only adds a 3-byte (24-bit) number to another of the same size, but also subtracts another 3-byte number from the sum of the first two. The purpose of the program is to introduce the general principle of multi-byte working; when you have more experience of programming techniques, e.g., the 'looping' techniques in Chapter 5, you can simplify the program and reduce its length.

The program can quite easily be modified to handle addition of values up to 48 bits in length (3 words) by changing some of the instructions, in much the same way as the 1-byte add and subtract program was modified to deal with adding and subtracting one word.

The program is in Listing 4.5. The data for the program is contained in the table labelled VALUE in line 8. The first three bytes in the table form the 24-bit augend C9C8C7H, and the next three bytes form the 24-bit addend 545352H. The remaining three bytes form a 24-bit subtrahend 808182H, which is to be subtracted from the sum of the augend and addend. The sum of the augend and addend is

augend   C9C8C7

addend   545352

------

sum   11E1C19

That is, the sum of the two 24-bit numbers is a 25-bit number! The program must therefore handle the carry from the final byte as though it were part of the addition. There are a number of ways of handling this problem, one method being illustrated in the program.

```
 1: ;****LISTING 4.5 – MULTIBYTE ADD AND SUBTRACT****
 2: ;****STACK SEGMENT****
 3: MY_STACK    SEGMENT PARA                               STACK
 4:             DB      100H        DUP(?)
 5: MY_STACK    ENDS
 6: ;****DATA SEGMENT****
 7: MY_DATA SEGMENT
 8: VALUE   DB      0C9H,0C8H,0C7H,54H,53H,52H,80H,81H,82H
 9: RESULT  DB      8           DUP(00H)
10: MY_DATA ENDS
11: ;****CODE SEGMENT****
12: MY_CODE SEGMENT
13: ASSUME  CS:MY_CODE,DS:MY_DATA,SS:MY_STACK
14: START:  MOV     AX,MY_DATA
15:         MOV     DS,AX           ;INITIALIZE DS
16:         LEA     BX,VALUE        ;BX POINTS TO BASE OF VALUE TABLE
17:         LEA     DI,RESULT       ;DI POINTS TO BASE OF RESULT TABLE
18:         SUB     AX,AX           ;CLEAR REGISTER AX
19:         CLC                     ;CLEAR THE CARRY FLAG FOR ADDITION
20:         MOV     AL,[BX+2]       ;GET L.S. AUGEND BYTE (C7H)
21:         ADC     AL,[BX+5]       ;ADD L.S. ADDEND BYTE (52H)
22:         MOV     [DI+3],AL       ;STORE L.S. SUM BYTE
23:         MOV     AL,[BX+1]       ;GET MIDDLE BYTE AUGEND (C8H)
24:         ADC     AL,[BX+4]       ;ADD MIDDLE BYTE ADDEND (53H)
25:         MOV     [DI+2],AL       ;STORE MIDDLE SUM BYTE
26:         MOV     AL,[BX]         ;GET M.S. BYTE AUGEND (49H)
27:         ADC     AL,[BX+3]       ;ADD M.S. BYTE ADDEND (54H)
28:         MOV     [DI+1],AL       ;STORE M.S. SUM BYTE
29:         MOV     AL,0H           ;CLEAR AL
30:         ADC     AL,AL           ;GET CARRY IN AL
31:         MOV     [DI],AL         ;SAVE CARRY
32:         CLC                     ;CLEAR CARRY FOR SUBTRACTION
33:         MOV     AL,[DI+3]       ;GET L.S. BYTE MINUEND FROM RESULT
34:         SBB     AL,[BX+8]       ;SUBTRACT L.S. SUBTRAHEND (82H)
```

```
35:      MOV     [DI+7],AL        ;STORE L.S. DIFFERENCE BYTE
36:      MOV     AL,[DI+2]        ;GET MIDDLE BYTE MINUEND
37:      SBB     AL,[BX+7]        ;SUBTRACT MIDDLE SUBTRAHEND (81H)
38:      MOV     [DI+6],AL        ;STORE MIDDLE DIFFERENCE BYTE
39:      MOV     AL,[DI+1]        ;GET M.S. BYTE MINUEND
40:      SBB     AL,[BX+6]        ;SUBTRACT M.S. SUBTRAHEND (80H)
41:      MOV     [DI+5],AL        ;STORE M.S. DIFFERENCE BYTE
42:      MOV     AL,[DI]          ;GET CARRY BIT FROM 1st ADD
43:      SBB     AL,0H            ;DEAL WITH BORROW BIT
44:      MOV     [DI+4],AL        ;SAVE BORROW
45:      INT     23H              ;RETURN CONTROL TO KEYBOARD
46: MY_CODE  ENDS                 ;END OF CODE SEGMENT
47: END      START                ;END OF PROGRAM
```

The subtraction part of the program subtracts the 24-bit subtrahend from the 25-bit sum as follows:

minuend	11 E 1 C 19
subtrahend	8 0 8 1 8 2
difference	09D9A97

Since the sum and the difference each need more than three bytes to store them, eight bytes are reserved in the data segment by line 9 of Listing 4.5 to save them. The results are to be placed in the table labelled RESULT, which is initialized with zero in every location.

Lines 14 and 15 of the program initialize the data segment, and line 16 Loads the Effective Address (LEA) of the first item of data in the table labelled VALUE into register BX (this address is, of course, calculated by the assembler program). Using the address in BX, any item in the VALUE table can be accessed by simply adding an 'offset' to the base address. Thus the item of data at address [BX] is the first item in the table, the item of data at address [BX + 1] is the second item, etc.

Similarly, the 16-bit effective address of the table labelled RESULT is loaded into register DI by line 17. As before, a result can be saved in, say, the fourth location of the RESULT table by MOVing the result to address [DI + 3].

Before commencing the addition part of the program, line 18 performs the routine operation of clearing register AX; although not strictly necessary, this has been done as a matter of normal 'housekeeping'. In line 19, the carry flag is cleared by a CLC (CLear Carry flag) instruction; this instruction is important because the program uses the ADC (ADd with Carry) instruction throughout, and the first stage of addition does not have a 'carry-in' into it.

The MOV, ADC, MOV group of instructions in lines 20–22, inclusive, is repeated several times, and is the basis of the multi-byte addition program. The MOV instruction in line 20 MOVes data from the third location in the table VALUE into register AL, see Fig. 4.1(a). Next the ADC AL,[BX + 5] instruction in line 21 not only adds the sixth value in the table VALUE to the number in AL but also adds the bit in the CF to the l.s.b. of the sum. The function of the ADC instruction is described as follows:

$$\text{destination} = \text{destination} + \text{source} + (CF)$$

After this instruction has been executed, register AL contains the sum of C7H, 52H and the content of the carry flag (which is zero at this stage). The result is

$$(AL) = 19H$$

and

$$(CF) = 1$$

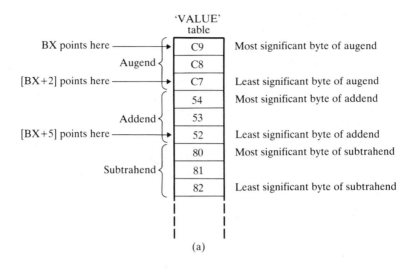

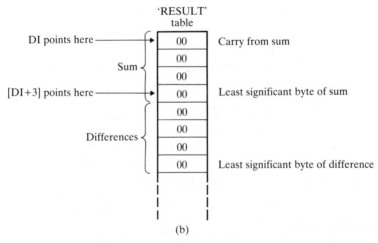

Figure 4.1 Tables in the data segment

Line 22 of the program saves this result in the fourth location in the RESULT table (see Fig. 4.1(b)).

Program lines 23–28, inclusive, add the next two bytes (with carry) and store the results in the RESULT table (the table being organized so that the result reads normally, i.e., the least significant byte of the result is at the right-hand side as you view the print-out of the data segment).

Since the addition of the most significant bytes of the augend and the addend produce a carry, it is necessary to extract the bit stored in the carry flag and save it in the correct position in the result table. This operation is completed in lines 29–31, inclusive, as follows. The MOV AL,0H instruction in line 29 clears register AL, and the ADC AL,AL instruction in line 30 adds the contents of register AL not only to itself $(0 + 0 = 0!)$ but also to the content of the CF. At the end of this sequence AL contains the carry bit; this is stored at the 'top' of the RESULT table by the instruction in line 31.

The instructions in lines 32–44, inclusive, subtract the 24-bit number 808182H from the 32-bit sum of the addition described above. The subtraction is performed using the SBB (SuBtract with Borrow) instruction; the operation performed by this instruction is

$$\text{destination} = \text{destination} - \text{source} - \text{content of CF}$$

The subtraction performed by the program is

$$010E1C19H - 808182H = 9D9A97H$$

On the completion of the program in Listing 4.5, the contents of the 17 bytes in the data segment are

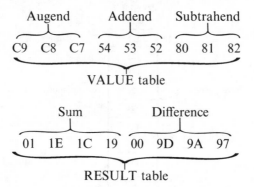

4.10   Multiplication

When two numbers of equal 'length' are multiplied, the produce can be twice as 'long' as the largest number. For this reason, the *product register* must be twice as long as either the multiplicand or the multiplier register. When an 8-bit produce is handled, the produce must be stored in a 16-bit register; when a 16-bit multiplication is handled, the produce can be up to 32 bits in length, and must be stored in two 16-bit registers. A diagram representing these operations is shown in Fig. 4.2.

Listing 4.6 contains a program handling the *unsigned multiplication* and *division* of two 8-bit numbers (the division process is discussed in Section 4.11).

```
 1:   ;****LISTING 4.6 – 8-BIT MULTIPLY AND DIVIDE
 2:   ;****STACK SEGMENT****
 3:   MY_STACK          SEGMENT PARA STACK
 4:                     DB    100H DUP(?)
 5:   MY_STACK          ENDS                        ;END OF STACK SEGMENT
 6:   ;****DATA SEGMENT****
 7:   MY_DATA           SEGMENT
 8:   VAL_1             DB 81H
 9:   VAL_2             DB 41H
10:   PROD              DW(?)
11:   ANS               DW(?)
12:   REM               DW(?)
13:   MY_DATA ENDS                     ;END OF DATA SEGMENT
14:   ;****CODE SEGMENT****
15:   MY_CODE SEGMENT
16:   ASSUME            CS:MY_CODE,DS:MY_DATA,SS:MY_STACK
17:   START:            MOV AX,MY_DATA        ;THESE TWO INSTRUCTIONS
18:                     MOV DS,AX             ;INITIALIZE (DS)
19:                     MOV AX,0H             ;CLEAR (AX)
20:                     MOV AL,VAL_1          ;LOAD MULTIPLICAND INTO AL
21:                     MOV CL,VAL_2          ;LOAD MULTIPLIER INTO CL
22:                     MUL CL                ;MULTIPLY
23:                     MOV PROD,AX           ;STORE PRODUCT
24:                     MOV AX,0H             ;CLEAR AX
25:                     MOV DX,0H             ;CLEAR DX
26:                     MOV AL,VAL_1          ;LOAD DIVIDEND
27:                     DIV CL                ;DIVIDE
28:                     MOV ANS,AX            ;STORE QUOTIENT (AL) AND REMAINDER (AH)
29:                     INT 23H               ;RETURN CONTROL TO KEYBOARD
30:   MY_CODE           ENDS                  ;END OF CODE SEGMENT
31:   END               START                 ;END OF PROGRAM
```

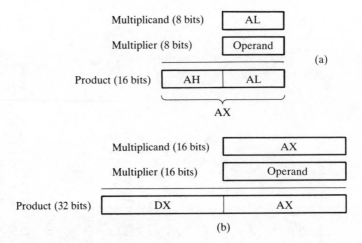

Figure 4.2 (a) 8-bit multiplication; (b) 16-bit multiplication.

In unsigned 8-bit multiplication, the multiplicand is loaded into register AL (see program line 20 and Fig. 4.2(a)); in 16-bit multiplication, it is loaded into register AX (see Fig. 4.2(b)). The unsigned multiplication mnemonic is

MUL source

where the 'source' (the multiplier) may either be stored in a register or in a memory location, or it may simply be a number. In Listing 4.6, the multiplier (VAL_2) is transferred to register CL, and the MUL CL instruction in line 22 performs the calculation

$$(AL) \times (CL) = 81H \times 41H = 20C1H$$

That is, after line 22 the value in AX is 20C1H. Line 23 stores the product in the 2-byte word space allocated to PROD (see also line 10).

Additionally, if the most significant 8 bits of the product contains a non-zero result (as it does in this case), the CPU sets both the CF and the OF to '1'; if the upper half of the result is zero, the CF and OF are cleared.

If you wish to perform 16-bit unsigned multiplication, the multiplicand is moved into AX (see Fig. 4.2(b)), and the 32-bit product is stored in registers DX and AX (AX containing the least significant 16 bits). Once again, the CPU records whether the upper 16 bits are zero by the method outlined above.

Unfortunately, *signed binary (or hex) multiplication* does not give the correct answer if the MUL instruction is used, and a special signed binary multiplication instruction must be used. This is known as Integer MULtiplication, whose mnemonic is IMUL; examples of this instruction are IMUL BL and IMUL BX.

The 8086 and 8088 cannot perform *multiplication of packed BCD (decimal) numbers*, because the BCD result cannot be extracted by means of a simple

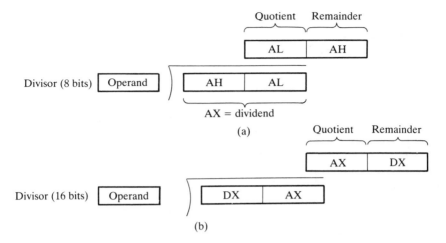

Figure 4.3   (a) 8-bit division; (b) 16-bit division.

decimal adjustment instruction (as it can for addition and subtraction). To perform decimal multiplication, you need to use some other representation such as unpacked BCD. The 8086 and 8088 instruction set contains an ASCII Adjust Multiplication (AAM) and ASCII Adjust Division (AAD) instruction, allowing you to perform decimal multiplication (see Chapter 10 for an example of multiplication of decimal numbers).

4.11   Division

Division is performed in the 8086 and 8088 in much the same manner as it is taught in the first year at school. For example, if you perform the calculation 72/60, the answer is a quotient of 1 and a remainder of 12; that is, the CPU stores the *quotient* and the *remainder* separately. The basis of 8-bit and 16-bit division is shown in Fig. 4.3.

Listing 4.6 illustrates an *8-bit unsigned division* program; the stages involved are:

1. The 8-bit dividend is MOVed into AL (see line 26), the dividend being extended to double length by MOVing zero into AH (see line 24).
2. The dividend is divided by the divisor by the DIV instruction (see line 27), the 'source' of the data being either in a memory, or in a register, or possibly being simply a number. In this case, register CL contains VAL_2. The quotient of the division is in AL and the remainder is in AH.
3. The quotient and remainder are saved in the word location ANS in the data segment by the MOV ANS,AX instruction in line 28.

When the program in Listing 4.6 has been run, the data segment contains the following eight bytes.

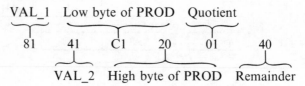

That is, the CPU records that $81/41 = 1$ and a remainder of 40.

When dealing with *signed binary (or hex) division*, the CPU could take either of two options. For example, when dividing -25 by $+8$, it could either say that the result is

a quotient of -4 and a remainder of $+7$

or

a quotient of -3 and a remainder of -1

Both answers are equally correct, but the 8086 and 8088 have been designed to give the second option, that is the *quotient and the remainder always have the same mathematical sign.*

The steps involved in using signed division differ from unsigned division insomuch that instead of MOVing zero into AH (for 8-bit division) or into DX (for 16-bit division), you need to *sign extend* the dividend into the higher register using one of the following instructions:

CBW ;Convert byte to word (sign extend 8 bits to 16 bits)
CWD ;Convert word to doubleword (sign extend 16 bits to 32 bits)
Thus the signed division process is performed by the following:

8-bit by 8-bit signed division
1. MOVe the dividend into AL.
2. Sign extend AL into AH (CBW).
3. Divide AX by the divisor.
16-bit by 16-bit signed division
1. MOVe the dividend into AX.
2. Sign extend AX into DX (CWD).
3. Divide DX,AX by the divisor.

As with decimal multiplication, *decimal division* cannot be performed directly, since the packed BCD result is confused with the cross-terms produced. Decimal division must therefore be performed using unpacked BCD values.

4.12   Logical and other instructions

The 8086 and 8088 logical instructions are described below.

OR   ;destination = destination OR source

XOR   ;destination = destination XOR source

AND   ;destination = destination AND source

TEST   ;ANDs the destination with the source; the result is
         discarded and the flags are updated by the AND operation.

In each of the above cases, the CF and OF are cleared and the AF is undefined.
The logical NOT instruction is described below.

NOT ;destination = NOT destination

The NOT instruction does not affect the flags.

The OR, XOR and AND instructions perform logical operations on a bit-by-
bit basis between the source operand and the destination operand, leaving the
result in the destination. The general expression for a logical operation is in the
form

logical operation (OR, XOR, AND) destination,source

Examples are to be found in lines 20, 21, 23, 25, 27 and 31 of Listing 4.7. To
illustrate the operation of the logical instructions, consider the case where the
values VAL_1 = 55H and VAL_2 = 33H are used as the destination and
source operands, respectively, with VAL_1 being stored in AL. The result of the
OR AL,VAL_2 instruction is

$$(AL) = VAL\_1 = 0101\ 0101B$$

$$VAL\_2 = 0011\ 0011B$$

$$OR\ AL,VAL\_2 = 0111\ 0111B = 77H$$

You will observe that the ORing operation is done on a bit-by-bit basis; that is,
the l.s.b. of VAL_1 is ORed with the l.s.b. of VAL_2, the next higher bit of
VAL_1 is ORed with the next higher bit of VAL_2, etc., until the two words
have been ORed. The result (77H) is left in the destination (AL).

Using the same values for the exclusive-OR (XOR) instruction, the result is

$$XOR\ AL,VAL\_2 = 0110\ 0110B = 66H$$

In this case, the XOR operation causes a logic '1' in the destination to *invert* the
corresponding bit in the source, and a logic '0' in the destination leaves the
corresponding source bit unchanged.

The AND instruction produces the following result:

$$AND\ AL,VAL\_2 = 0001\ 0001B = 11H$$

In general, the OR function is useful for *setting* specified bits in a logic word to
'1'; the XOR function is useful either for *clearing* selected bits or for *logically
inverting* selected bits; the AND function is useful for *masking* (see also Chapter
7) and *clearing* specified bits.

```
 1:  ;****LISTING 4.7 – LOGICAL AND OTHER INSTRUCTIONS
 2:  ;****STACK SEGMENT****
 3:  MY_STACK         SEGMENT PARA    STACK
 4:                   DB      100H    DUP(?)
 5:  MY_STACK         ENDS
 6:  ;****DATA SEGMENT****
 7:  MY_DATA          SEGMENT
 8:  TEST_1           DB      0FH
 9:  TEST_2           DB      0FAH
10:  TEST_3           DB      0AAH
11:  TEST_4           DB      8H
12:  RESULT           DB      5       DUP(11H)
13:  MY_DATA ENDS
14:  ;****CODE SEGMENT****
15:  MY_CODE          SEGMENT
16:  ASSUME  SS:MY_STACK,DS:MY_DATA,CS:MY_CODE
17:  START:  MOV     AX,MY_DATA
18:          MOV     DS,AX
19:          LEA     BX,RESULT       ;BX POINTS TO RESULT TABLE
20:          XOR     AX,AX           ;CLEAR REGISTER AX AND CF AND OF
21:          OR      AL,TEST_1       ;LOGIC OR AX WITH TEST_1
22:          MOV     [BX],AL         ;SAVE RESULT IN 1st LOCATION IN RESULT TABLE
23:          AND     AL,TEST_2       ;LOGIC AND AX WITH TEST_2
24:          MOV     [BX+1],AL       ;SAVE RESULT IN 2nd LOCATION
25:          XOR     AL,TEST_3       ;EXCLUSIVE-OR AL WITH TEST_3
26:          MOV     [BX+2],AL       ;SAVE RESULT IN 3rd LOCATION
27:          NOT     AL              ;FORM 1s COMPLEMENT OF AL
28:          MOV     [BX+3],AL       ;SAVE IT IN 4th LOCATION
29:          NEG     AL              ;FORM 2s COMPLEMENT OF AL
30:          MOV     [BX+4],AL       ;SAVE IT IN 5TH LOCATION
31:          TEST    AL,TEST_4       ;TEST TO SEE IF BIT 3 = '1'
32:                                  ;THE CONTENTS OF AL BEING UNCHANGED
33:          CMP     AL,0FH          ;COMPARE AL WITH 0FH
34:          CMP     AL,0A1H         ;COMPARE AL WITH 0A1H
35:          INT     23H
36:  MY_CODE ENDS
37:  END     START
```

The XOR function is also useful for clearing the contents of a register and, simultaneously, clearing the CF and OF; for example, this is done by XOR AL,AL.

The test instruction can be used to test the state of a bit in a word without altering the state of the word. For example, if AL contains A1H and it is tested with TEST_4, where TEST_4 = 8H, the instruction TEST AL,TEST_4 does the following (see also line 31 of Listing 4.7):

1. it ANDs A1H (1010 0001B) with 8H (0000 1000B),
2. it discards the result, leaving A1H in AL,
3. it sets or clears the flags according to the AND operation.

That is, it TESTs the state of bit 3 of the destination (AL) and, since the result of the AND operation is 00H, the CPU sets the zero flag to indicate that bit 3 of the destination (AL) is zero. The TEST instruction is used in conjunction with a 'jump' instruction in many programs (see Chapter 5 for information about jump instructions).

The logical NOT function logically inverts or complements the value in the destination operand; that is, it turns each '0' in the word into a '1', and each '1' into a '0'. Hence, if AL contains 01010101B, then the instruction NOT AL (see line 27 of Listing 4.7) leaves AL containing 10101010B. The result of the NOT instruction is known as the *1s complement* of the original data.

Although not strictly a logical instruction, the NEG instruction (see line 29 of Listing 4.7) generates the *negative value* or *2s complement* of the destination operand. The process of obtaining the 'negative' value of a number is to form the 1s complement (see above) and then add '1' to the l.s.b. of the number. For example, if $X = 0101\ 0101B$, then

$$-X = 1010\ 1010 + 1 = 1010\ 1011B$$

If register AL contains 5FH then, after the NEG AL instruction, register AL contains A1H.

When subtracting numbers, the CPU evaluates the 2s complement of the subtrahend and, in order to subtract the subtrahend *it adds the 2s complement of the subtrahend to the minuend to give the difference.*

The CMP (CoMPare) instruction (see lines 33 and 34 of Listing 4.7) allows the CPU to compare the value of the destination operand with that of the source operand. The CMP instruction subtracts the source operand from the destination operand and updates the flags according to the result; the result is discarded. This is yet another method of testing whether a particular condition or value has been reached by the program.

For example, if register AL contains A1H, then the CMP AL,0FH instruction in line 33 of Listing 4.7 clears the carry flag; this is because A1H − 0FH is not zero. The CMP AL,A1H instruction in line 34 would set the zero flag because A1H − A1H = 0. The CMP instruction is usually used in association with a 'jump' instruction – see Chapter 5.

With the four test values TEST_1 to TEST_4, inclusive, in Listing 4.7, the nine bytes in the data segment when the program has been run are

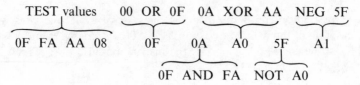

5
Jump, shift and rotate instructions

5.1 Types of jump instructions

Jump instructions allow the programmer to deviate from the normal sequential execution of instructions in the program, causing control to be transferred to some other point in the program. This feature is particularly useful when a choice is made between alternative paths which depend on the condition of data in the computer. For example, the program in the computer at your bank makes the decision whether to add an amount of money to your account or to take it away from it, and this depends on whether the cheque it is handling is a credit or a debit.

There are two broad categories of jump instruction, namely an unconditional jump and a conditional jump. An *unconditional jump* instruction causes the CPU to automatically transfer program control from its current position to another point in the program which does not follow in sequence. A *conditional jump* refers to a transfer of program control which takes place *after a particular condition has been tested* (it is frequently the condition of one of the flags which is tested), *and the result is found to be true*. There are many types of conditional jump, which are discussed as the chapter proceeds.

A jump or transfer of control instruction in the 8088 can be one of two kinds, namely intrasegment or intersegment. An *intrasegment jump* results in a transfer of control to an instruction whose address is within ± 32K of the jump instruction. This is the more usual type of jump, and simply involves the assembler calculating either an 8-bit or a 16-bit signed displacement from the jump address, and refers to an address within the current code segment.

An *intersegment jump* allows you to transfer control to an entirely new code segment. This type of jump instruction takes up five bytes of memory as follows: one byte is the opcode for the intersegment jump instruction, two bytes contain the base address of the new code segment (which is the new value to be put in the CS register), and the remaining two bytes contain the effective address to which control is transferred (which is placed in the IP register). Intersegment jumps are usually reserved, for example, for chaining one program with another remote program, or for requesting service from a supervisory program such as the DOS.

5.2 The unconditional jump instruction

The unconditional JuMP instruction (mnemonic JMP) causes an unconditional transfer to the jump *target address*. The jump instruction may be either a direct jump or an indirect jump. A *direct jump* instruction specifies the jump target in the instruction itself, e.g., JMP JUMP_2 (see line 22 of Listing 5.1). When used in this way, the jump target is defined by a label, the label name being used as the jump operand. The assembler program calculates the displacement in bytes between the current instruction and the target, and uses this figure to determine where program control is to be transferred to.

If the target is within $+127$ or -128 bytes of the JMP instruction, the assembler uses a SHORT JMP instruction. Otherwise the assembler uses a 16-bit displacement, allowing the program to access any target within a $\pm 32K$ range.

If the target is outside the current code segment, the assembler generates an intersegment JMP instruction. In this case the operand is four bytes in length, and specifies both the new code segment base and the offset of the target within the new code segment.

The *indirect JMP* instruction enables you to evaluate the target address dynamically by storing it in a 16-bit register, e.g., JMP CX. In this way, the displacement is calculated and stored in CX before the jump is taken.

5.3 Conditional jump instructions

These allow you to test a specific condition, and the jump is not made until the condition is satisfied. If the condition is not satisfied, the program continues sequentially. The conditions tested generally involve the flags although, as described later, there are some conditional jump instructions which test the state of the CX register.

Listing 5.1 contains a selection of conditional jump instructions. This is a useful program to run under the control of the single-stepping facility of DEBUG, and illustrates the decision-making process involved at each stage.

The range of conditional jump instructions in the 8088 are listed in Table 5.1. The instruction mnemonic is intended to describe the condition tested; in some cases, optional mnemonics are available. For example, the conditional jump instruction JC has optional mnemonics JNAE and JB, each having its own meaning.

```
 1: ;****JUMP INSTRUCTIONS – LISTING 5.1****
 2: ;****STACK SEGMENT****
 3: MY_STACK              SEGMENT  PARA    STACK
 4:              DB       100H     DUP(?)
 5: MY_STACK              ENDS
 6: ;****CODE SEGMENT****
 7: MY_CODE SEGMENT
 8:              ASSUME  SS:MY_STACK,CS:MY_CODE
 9: START:       XOR      AX,AX   ;CLEAR AX, CF AND OF
10:              JNC      JUMP_1  ;JUMP IF NO CARRY
11: JUMP_2:      JZ       JUMP_3  ;JUMP IF ZERO
12: JUMP_4:      JMP      JUMP_5  ;UNCONDITIONAL JUMP
13: JUMP_6:      JNZ      JUMP_7  ;JUMP IF NON-ZERO
14: JUMP_8:      JPE      JUMP_9  ;JUMP IF PARITY EVEN
15: JUMP_10:     JPO      JUMP_11 ;JUMP IF PARITY ODD
16: JUMP_12:     ADD      AX,8000H ;SET SIGN BIT
17:              JNS      JUMP_13 ;JUMP IF NO SIGN BIT
18: JUMP_14:     JS       JUMP_15 ;JUMP IF SIGN BIT SET
19: JUMP_16:     XOR      AX,AX   ;CLEAR AX, CF AND OF
20:              JNO      JUMP_17 ;JUMP ON NO OVERFLOW
21: JUMP_18:     INT      23H     ;RETURN CONTROL TO KEYBOARD
22: JUMP_1:      JMP      JUMP_2  ;RETURN
23: JUMP_3:      JMP      JUMP_4
24: JUMP_5:      INC      AX      ;(AX) = 1
25:              JMP      JUMP_6
26: JUMP_7:      JMP      JUMP_8
27: JUMP_9:      JMP      JUMP_10
28: JUMP_11:     JMP      JUMP_12
29: JUMP_13:     JMP      JUMP_14
30: JUMP_15:     JMP      JUMP_16
31: JUMP_17:     JMP      JUMP_18
32: MY_CODE      ENDS
33: END          START
```

The JCXZ instruction transfers control to the target operand if the content of register CX is zero. This instruction is sometimes useful at the beginning of an instruction loop to cause the loop to be bypassed if CX contains zero; it can be used, for example, to prevent the computer from issuing an invoice to a customer who does not owe your company any money!

At this point you should run the program in Listing 5.1 in the single-stepping mode and study the effect of each instruction.

5.4 LOOP instructions

When handling repetitive loops, it is useful to have instructions which test the state of a 'loop counter' and, so long as the content of the counter is non-zero, cause the program loop to be repeated. Register CX has a range of LOOP instructions associated with it for this purpose, which are listed in Table 5.2. An

Table 5.1   Summary of conditional jump instructions

Instruction mnemonic	Condition for jump	Meaning ("Jump if ")
JE/JZ	ZF = 1	equal/zero
JNE/JNZ	ZF = 0	not equal/not zero
JL/JNGE	(SF XOR OF) = 1	less than/not greater or equal
JNL/JGE	(SF XOR OF) = 0	not less or equal/greater than
JG/JNLE	((SF XOR OF) OR ZF) = 0	greater/not less or equal
JNG/JLE	((SF XOR OF) OR ZF) = 1	not greater/less than or equal
JC/JB/JNAE	CF = 1	carry/below/not above or equal
JNC/JNB/JAE	CF = 0	no carry/not below/above or equal
JA/JNBE	(CF OR ZF) = 0	above/not below or equal
JNA/JBE	(CF OR ZF) = 1	not above/below or equal
JS	SF = 1	sign flag set
JNS	SF = 0	no sign
JO	OF = 1	overflow flag set
JNO	OF = 0	no overflow
JP/JPE	PF = 1	parity flag set/parity even
JNP/JPO	PF = 0	no parity/parity odd
JCXZ	(CX) = 0	register CX contains zero

Table 5.2   LOOP instructions

Instruction mnemonic	Meaning ("LOOP . . .")	Operation
LOOP	if CX not zero	CX = CX − 1. Loop (jump) if (CX) not zero, else continue sequentially.
LOOPE / LOOPZ	while equal to zero	CX = CX − 1. Loop if (CX) not zero AND (ZF) = 1, else continue sequentially.
LOOPNE / LOOPNZ	while not equal to zero	CX = CX − 1. Loop if (CX) not zero AND (ZF) = 0, else continue sequentially.

```
LISTING 5.2
25: DELAY   PROC
26:         MOV    CX,100       ;NUMBER OF CYCLES OF OUTER LOOP
27: LONG:   MOV    DX,39800     ;DATA FOR INNER LOOP
28: TEST:   DEC    DX
29:         JNZ    TEST         ;END OF INNER LOOP
30:         LOOP   LONG         ;END OF OUTER LOOP
31:         RET
```

example of the use of the LOOP instruction is contained in Listing 5.2 (see also Section 5.5).

5.5   An application of conditional jump and LOOP instructions

A popular application of conditional jump instructions is in a *software time delay*, which generates a known number of time-wasting operations. A flowchart

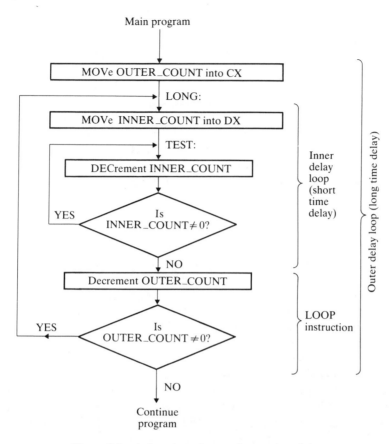

Figure 5.1   A flowchart for a software time delay

illustrating the way in which a time delay can be produced is shown in Fig. 5.1, and the associated program is in Listing 5.2.

The basis of the program is to load a register with a value known as a 'counter', the counter being decremented until its value reaches zero. Provided that you know the number of clock cycles per instruction (see Appendix A), and also the periodic time of the system clock, you can calculate the length of the time delay.

You can produce a short time delay using only the inner loop in Fig. 5.1 (the corresponding program lines in Listing 5.2 being 27, 28 and 29). The value which is moved into register DX controls the length of the 'short' time delay and, in the case of the computer used by the author, the value 39800 gave a delay of about 0.25 s. This value is decremented during each pass of the loop, and is tested by the JNZ instruction in line 29. If the content of register DX is non-zero at this time, control is transferred to the label TEST, and DX is decremented once more. Finally, when the content of DX is zero, an escape is made from the loop.

A longer time delay is obtained by *nesting loops within one another* (nesting is a process by which one loop calls for another loop and so on). In Fig. 5.1 (and Listing 5.2), register CX is used to store the OUTER_COUNT value. In this case a LOOP instruction is used to automatically decrement the contents of CX and to check if its value is non-zero. If this is the case, the outer loop is executed once more. This process continues until the content of CX is zero.

Provided that the inner loop gives a time delay of reasonable length, then the overall time delay is given approximately by the produce (OUTER_COUNT × delay of inner loop). In this case, the time delay is approximately $100 \times 0.25\,s = 25\,s$.

5.6 Shift instructions

Shift instructions are used to shift the contents of a register or a memory either to the 'left' or to the 'right'. Depending on the direction of the 'shift', the instructions provide an efficient mechanism for either multiplying or dividing a number in a register or memory by a multiple of two. The 8088 has three shift instructions, which are illustrated in Fig. 5.2.

The SHL (SHift logical Left) and SAL (Shift Arithmetic Left) are alternative mnemonics for the same instruction, namely to shift the content of a register or memory location to the left and insert a '0' into the least significant bit position; the bit in the CF is replaced by the m.s.b. of the shifted value. The instruction can be used to shift either a byte or a word, and the data which is shifted may be either in a register or in a memory. The mnemonic of the instruction is either

SAL destination,count

or

SHL destination, count

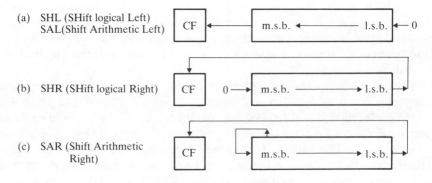

Figure 5.2 Shift instructions.

where the 'count' is the number of places the data is to be shifted. If the count is unity, then it can be specified directly in the instruction, e.g., SHL AL,1; this instruction shifts the contents of register AL one place to the left. If the count is more than unity, the shift 'number' must be loaded into register CL before using the instruction, as follows:

MOV CL,4

SHL AL,CL

Listing 5.3 demonstrates the use of all the shift and rotate instructions in the instruction set of the 8088 (the latter are described in Section 5.7). After reading this section and Section 5.7, you should run the program in the single-stepping mode and investigate the result at each stage (see also Section 5.8).

The SHR (SHift logical Right) – see Fig. 5.2(b) – logically shifts the data 'right' and inserts a '0' into the most significant bit position; it also shifts the least significant bit into the CF. This instruction is shown in Listing 5.3 using an SHR AL,CL instruction with CL = 1 (which is equivalent to SHR AL,1).

The SAR instruction – see Fig. 5.2(c) – Shifts the value Arithmetically to the Right; in an arithmetic shift right, the sign bit is retained and also extended to the right. If the sign bit is '0', then a '0' is entered into the most significant bit position each time the instruction is executed; if the sign bit is '1', then a '1' is entered into the most significant bit position (as is the case in Listing 5.3).

5.7 Rotate instructions

There are four 'rotate' instructions in the instruction set of the 8088, which are illustrated in Fig. 5.3. These instructions shift the data (which could be either a word or a byte which is stored either in a register or in a memory) in a 'rotating' fashion. In the case of ROL and ROR, the bit which is 'rotated' is also copied into the CF. The RCL and RCR instructions are, depending on the length of the operand, effectively a 9-bit or a 17-bit rotate instruction, with the CF participating in the operation.

5.8 Summary of the results of Listing 5.3

The program in Listing 5.3 highlights the general features of all the shift and rotate instructions in the instruction set of the 8088. Register AH is used in each case as a loop counter, so that each instruction is used ten times with the sample data. When running the program, you should also investigate the effect of these instructions on the flags (see also the instruction set in Appendix A). Table 5.3 lists the principal effects of each step in the program.

Both 'shift' and 'rotate' instructions can be used (within limits) as simple multiplication and division by 2 (or an integral multiple of 2). For example, shifting or rotating data 'left' one place effectively multiplies the data by 2, and shifting or rotating it 'right' one place effectively divides it by 2. However, you are warned that this has its limitations!

```
 1: ;****LISTING 5.3 – SHIFT AND ROTATE INSTRUCTIONS****
 2: ;****STACK SEGMENT****
 3: MY_STACK        SEGMENT    PARA    STACK
 4:
 5: MY_STACK        DB         100H    DUP(?)
 6: ;****CODE SEGMENT****        ENDS
 7: MY_CODE         SEGMENT
 8:                 ASSUME     CS:MY_CODE,SS:MY_STACK
 9: START:          NOP                 ;NOP TO EXAMINE REGISTERS
10:                 MOV        AL,1     ;SAMPLE DATA
11:                 MOV        AH,10    ;SET UP "SHIFT" COUNTER (DECIMAL 10)
12:                 MOV        CL,1
13:                 CLC                 ;CLEAR THE CARRY FLAG
14: LOOP1:          SHL        AL,1     ;SHIFT LOGICAL/ARITHMETIC LEFT = SAL
15:                 DEC        AH       ;DECREMENT "SHIFT" COUNTER
16:                 JNZ        LOOP1    ;JUMP IF "SHIFT" COUNTER NON-ZRO
17:                 MOV        AL,80H   ;SAMPLE DATA
18:                 MOV        AH,10
19:                 CLC
20: LOOP2:          SHR        AL,CL    ;SHIFT LOGICAL RIGHT
21:                 DEC        AH
22:                 JNZ        LOOP2
23:                 MOV        AL,80H   ;SAMPLE DATA
24:                 MOV        AH,10
25:                 CLC
26: LOOP3:          SAR        AL,1     ;SHIFT ARITHMETIC RIGHT
27:                 DEC        AH
28:                 JNE        LOOP3    ;JNE IS EQUIVALENT TO JNZ
29:                 MOV        AL,1H    ;SAMPLE DATA
30:                 MOV        AH,10
31:                 CLC
```

```
32: LOOP4:    ROL    AL,CL      ;ROTATE LEFT (8-BIT)
33:           DEC    AH
34:           JNE    LOOP4
35:           MOV    AL,1H      ;SAMPLE DATA
36:           MOV    AH,10
37:           CLC
38: LOOP5:    ROR    AL,1       ;ROTATE RIGHT (8-BIT)
39:           DEC    AH
40:           JNZ    LOOP5
41:           MOV    AL,80H     ;SAMPLE DATA
42:           MOV    AH,10
43:           CLC
44: LOOP6:    RCL    AL,1       ;ROTATE THROUGH CARRY LEFT (9-BIT)
45:           DEC    AH
46:           JNZ    LOOP6
47:           MOV    AL,1H      ;SAMPLE DATA
48:           MOV    AH,10
49:           CLC
50: LOOP7:    RCR    AL,1       ;ROTATE THROUGH CARRY RIGHT (9-BIT)
51:           DEC    AH
52:           JNZ    LOOP7
53:           INT    23H
54: MY_CODE   ENDS
55: END       START
```

Table 5.3 Effects of each step

Step	SHL		SHR		SAR		ROL		ROR		RCL		RCR	
	Data in AL	CF	Data in AL	CF	Data in AL	CF	Data in AL	CF	Data in AL	CF	Data in AL	CF	Data in AL	CF
Initial data	01	0	80	0	80	0	01	0	01	0	80	0	01	0
1	02	0	40	0	CO	0	02	0	80	1	00	1	00	1
2	04	0	20	0	E0	0	04	0	40	0	01	0	80	0
3	08	0	10	0	F0	0	08	0	20	0	02	0	40	0
4	10	0	08	0	F8	0	10	0	10	0	04	0	20	0
5	20	0	04	0	FC	0	20	0	08	0	08	0	10	0
6	40	0	02	0	FE	0	40	0	04	0	10	0	08	0
7	80	0	01	0	FF	0	80	0	02	0	20	0	04	0
8	00	1	00	1	FF	1	01	1	01	0	40	0	02	0
9	00	0	00	0	FF	1	02	0	80	1	80	0	01	0
10	00	0	00	0	FF	1	04	0	40	0	00	1	00	1

(a) ROL (ROtate Left with branch to carry)

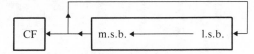

(b) ROR (ROtate Right with branch to carry)

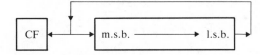

(c) RCL (Rotate through Carry Left)

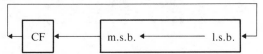

(d) RCR (Rotate through Carry Right)

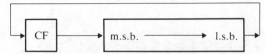

Figure 5.3 Rotate instructions.

6

The stack and subroutines

6.1 Introduction to the stack

The stack is an area of the RAM which is reserved for the purpose of saving data dynamically; that is, the data in a register or memory can be transferred to the stack for a period of time whilst that register or memory location is used for some other purpose. At a later point in time, the data can be restored to the originating register or memory location.

Figure 6.1 shows the memory map of the working area of the memory of an 8088. The assembler calculates the addresses of the code segment and the data segment (if any), and places the stack above them in the memory of the computer. When writing the program, *it is the programmer's responsibility* to make the stack large enough for the needs of the program. Unless the program is stack-intensive, about 100H bytes is usually enough space.

The CPU contains two 16-bit registers which relate to the stack, and are the base pointer (BP) and the stack pointer (SP) – see Fig. 6.1. The *base pointer* 'points' to the 'bottom', or the lowest location in the stack, and initially contains an offset relative to the stack segment register (SS) of 0000H. The *stack pointer* points to the 'top' of the stack and contains an offset corresponding to that asked for by the programmer when establishing the stack segment.

The program in Listing 6.1 requests 60H bytes for the stack (see line 4), which are all initially filled with 99H; the reason for using the latter value is that it does not conflict with any value used during the program; you can check the size of the stack before you run the main program by displaying the stack segment on the screen of the VDU. When the program is first run, the SP register contains the hex value 0060H. Hence, if the SS register contains 07FEH, the physical address of the initial 'top' of the stack is 07FE0 + 60 = 08040H.

The stack is a *Last-In, First-Out (LIFO)* store, and when an item of data is saved on the stack, it is transferred to the 'top' of the stack; when an item of data is removed from the stack, it is taken off the 'top' of the stack. That is, the last

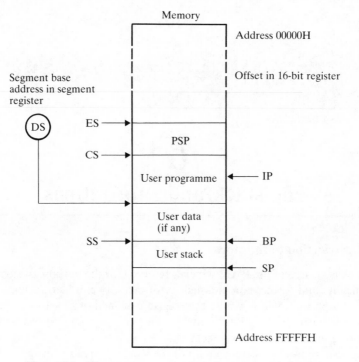

Figure 6.1 The memory map when the program is loaded

item to be added to the stack is the first item to be removed. Data is saved on the stack by means of a *PUSH* instruction, and is removed from the stack by a *POP* instruction, as described below.

6.2 The PUSH instruction

A PUSH instruction transfers a word (two bytes) from the source address to the top of the stack as follows (see Fig. 6.2 for PUSH AX):

1. The content of the SP is decremented to give a new 'top of stack'.
2. The *high byte* of the word being PUSHed is copied into the location at the new top of stack address.
3. The SP is decremented once more to give a new 'top' of stack.
4. The *low byte* of the word being PUSHed is copied into the new top of stack address.

Using the values in Fig. 6.2, the initial value in the stack pointer is 0060H (see also Section 6.1). Step 1 above decrements the SP from 0060H to 005FH, and step 2 stores the high byte (A1H) of register AX at this address. Step 3 decrements the SP to 005EH, and step 4 stores the low byte (2AH) of register AX into

```
 1: ;****USE OF THE STACK – LISTING 6.1****
 2: ;****STACK SEGMENT****
 3: MY_STACK              SEGMENT  PARA        STACK
 4:             DB        60H      DUP(99H)
 5: MY_STACK              ENDS
 6: ;****CODE SEGMENT****
 7: MY_CODE               SEGMENT
 8:             ASSUME    CS:MY_CODE,SS:MY_STACK
 9: START:      NOP
10:             MOV AX,0A12AH
11:             MOV BX,0B12BH
12:             MOV CX,0C12CH
13:             MOV DX,0D12DH
14:             PUSH AX               ;SAVE AV REG
15:             PUSH BX               ;SAVE BX REG
16:             PUSH CX               ;SAVE CX REG
17:             PUSH DX               ;SAVE DX REG
18:             XOR AX,AX             ;CLEAR AX
19:             XOR BX,BX             ;CLEAR BX
20:             XOR CX,CX             ;CLEAR CX
21:             XOR DX,DX             ;CLEAR DX
22:             POP DX                ;RESTORE DX
23:             POP CX                ;RESTORE CX
24:             POP AX                ;EXCHANGE (AX) WITH (BX)
25:             POP BX                ;DITTO
26:             INT 23H
27: MY_CODE               ENDS
28: END                   START
```

this offset address (corresponding to a physical address of 0803EH) – see Fig. 6.2(b).

By the time that line 17 of Listing 6.1 has been executed, the contents of registers AX, BX, CX and DX have been saved on the stack in the following sequence.

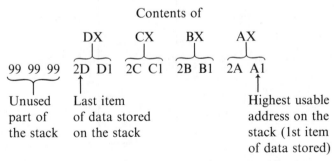

Contents of

DX   CX   BX   AX

99 99 99   2D D1   2C C1   2B B1   2A A1

Unused   Last item   Highest usable
part of   of data stored   address on the
the stack   on the stack   stack (1st item
                                     of data stored)

You will find that, in practice, the part of the stack which is described above as 'unused' may (if you are using DEBUG) contain values other than 99H. The reason is that the computer itself (i.e., the DEBUG utility) also uses the stack.

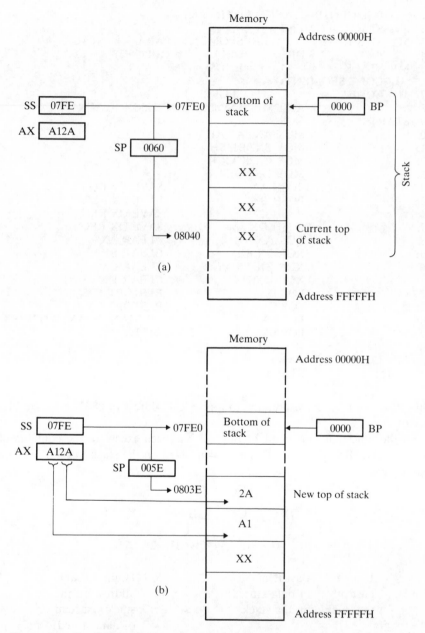

Figure 6.2 Conditions (a) before a PUSH AX instruction, (b) after PUSH AX.

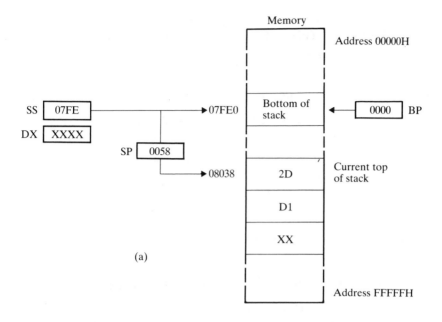

(a)

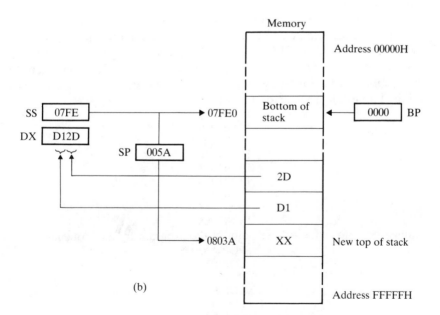

(b)

Figure 6.3   Conditions (a) before a POP DX instruction, (b) after POP DX.

It is of interest to note that the location at the initial top of the stack, i.e., address 07FEDH + 60H is never used to store valid data, i.e., it always contains electronic 'garbage'.

6.3 The POP instruction

The POP instruction transfers a word (two bytes) from the top of the stack to the destination as follows (see Fig. 6.3 for POP DX):

1. It POPs the byte of data at the current top of the stack into the *low byte* of the destination.
2. It increments the SP register to form a new top of stack.
3. It POPs the byte of data at the new top of the stack into the *high byte* of the destination.
4. It increments the SP register to form a new 'top' of stack.

6.4 Points to note about PUSH and POP instructions

1. In general, each PUSH instruction is associated with a POP instruction at a later point in the program (failure to observe this fact will cause erratic behaviour of the program).
2. A PUSH and POP sequence ensures a return of the SP to the original top of the stack, i.e., the contents of the SP are unchanged after this sequence.
3. When the status of the CPU has been 'saved' by means of a series of PUSH instructions, *it must be restored* by the reverse sequence of POP instructions. For example, if the following sequence of PUSH instructions is used to save all the important registers on the stack,

```
                    PUSH ES
                    PUSH DS
                    PUSH SI
                    PUSH DI
                    PUSH BP
                    PUSH DX
                    PUSH CX
                    PUSH BX
                    PUSH AX
```

it must be followed at a later point in the program by the sequence

```
                    POP AX
                    POP BX
                    POP CX
                    POP DX
                    POP BP
                    POP DI
                    POP SI
                    POP DS
                    POP ES
```

Table 6.1 Summary of the results of Listing 6.1

Register	Before PUSH	After POP
AX	A12A	B12B
BX	B12B	A12A
CX	C12C	C12C
DX	D12D	D12D

You can, according to the needs of the program, save and restore only one register or a selected combination of registers. Two of the PUSH and POP sequences in Listing 6.1 have been reversed; you will find that when you run the program, the contents of registers AX and BX have been exchanged!

The contents of the four 16-bit registers used in Listing 6.1 before the PUSH operations and after the POP operations are given in Table 6.1.

6.5 Subroutines and procedures

A *subroutine* is a block of instructions which are used several times by the main program. The instructions may be, for example, to examine the stock of an item in a warehouse. It would be very inefficient in terms not only of memory usage but also of the programmer's time to insert the block of instructions in the main program each time it is needed. By writing the block of instructions as a subroutine, it can be 'called for' by the main program at any point.

There are two ways of calling for a subroutine: one is by calling for part of the program commencing at the address at which the first instruction in the subroutine lies; the second is to give the subroutine a 'name' and then call for the named subroutine. A named subroutine is known as a *procedure*, and if you have named the procedure PROC1, the assembly language instruction which transfers control to the procedure is

CALL PROC1

You should note that you must not leave a space in the procedure name; that is, PROC1 cannot be called PROC 1, but it can be called PROC_1. The general mechanics of operation of a procedure are as shown in Fig. 6.4.

When the program is assembled, the computer knows the address of PROC1, and when the CPU meets a CALL PROC1 instruction in the main program, it simply places the address of PROC1 in the appropriate registers (we will deal with the difference between intrasegment and intersegment CALLs later), and transfers control to that address (see 1st CALL in Fig. 6.4).

However, the CPU must not lose track of the position it has reached in the main program, and on completion of the procedure it must return to the next instruction in the main program (which is the MOV AH,AL instruction in Fig. 6.4). The way in which the CPU handles this situation is to save the 'return'

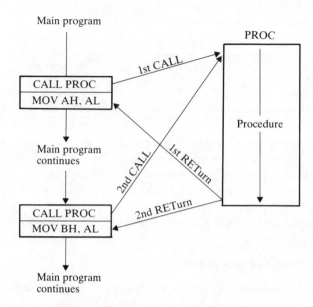

Figure 6.4   Operation of a procedure.

address on the stack. In the following, we will assume that PROC1 is in the same code segment as the main program, so that the offset of PROC1 is specified by a 16-bit value, and we will suppose also that this offset is 100H.

If the CALL PROC1 instruction (which is a three-byte instruction if the procedure is within the same code segment as the main program) lies at address 000AH, the CPU PUSHes the 16-bit address 000A + 3 = 000DH onto the stack (it pushes the high byte first); this is the address of the 'next' instruction in the main program. At the same time, the 16-bit value 0100H is placed in the IP, so that the next instruction to be executed is at that address, corresponding to the address of the first instruction in the procedure.

When the computer has completed the procedure, the hex value 000DH is POPped off the stack and into the IP. This means that the MOV AH,AL instruction at this address is executed next.

As illustrated in Fig. 6.4, the procedure can be called more than once and, each time it is called, the return address to the main program is PUSHed into the stack. On completion of the procedure, the return address is POPped off the stack and into the IP, allowing the main program to continue normally.

6.6   Intrasegment and intersegment CALL instructions

There are two types of CALL instruction, namely NEAR and FAR, depending respectively on whether the call is intrasegment or intersegment. When writing the program, the programmer tells the assembler which type of CALL he is using (although this is optional with intrasegment CALLs). A NEAR-type CALL is one which lies within ± 32K of the CALLing instruction, and is specified either by

PROC1   PROC   NEAR

or

PROC1   PROC

A FAR-type call is specified by

PROC2   PROC   FAR

An important difference between the two is that in a NEAR-type CALL (intrasegment), only the two bytes in the IP are pushed onto the stack; in a FAR-type CALL (intersegment), four bytes are pushed onto the stack. In the latter case, the four bytes comprise the contents of the IP and the contents of the CS register; the CPU needs the four bytes in order to calculate the 20-bit return address to the CALLing program.

6.7   Organization of subroutines and procedures

A procedure can be subdivided into the four sections shown in Fig. 6.5.

On entering a procedure, it may be necessary to save the contents of certain register and memory locations (these locations may be used by the procedure itself). This is done in stage 1 by PUSHing them onto the stack.

The second stage of the procedure is essential, since it contains the group of instructions which are CALLed for by the main program.

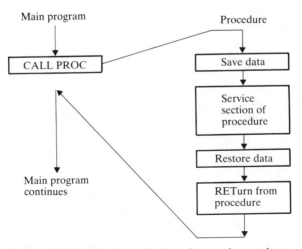

Figure 6.5 Organization of subroutines and procedures.

```
 1: ;****A PROGRAM USING PROCEDURES – LISTING 6.2****
 2: ;****STACK SEGMENT****
 3: MY_STACK              SEGMENT  PARA       STACK
 4:                DB     60H      DUP(99H)
 5: MY_STACK              ENDS
 6: ;****DATA SEGMENT****
 7: MY_DATA SEGMENT
 8: RESULT_1              DW       (OH)
 9: RESULT_2              DW       (OH)
10: MY_DATA ENDS
11: ;****CODE SEGMENT****
12: MY_CODE SEGMENT
13:               ASSUME   CS:MY_CODE,SS:MY_STACK,DS:MY_DATA
14: START:        NOP
15:               MOV AX,1111H
16:               MOV BX,2222H
17:               MOV CX,4444H
18:               CALL     PROC1
19:               CALL     PROC3       ;CALL PROCEDURE PROC3
20:               INT 23H
21: ;****PROC1****
22: PROC1         PROC     NEAR
23:               PUSH     AX          ;SAVE (AX) ON THE STACK
24:               ADD      AX,BX
25:               MOV      RESULT_1,AX  ;SAVE (AX) IN RESULT_1
26:               NOP                   ;FOR USE LATER
27:               POP      AX          ;RESTORE (AX) TO ORIGINAL VALUE
28:               RET
29: PROC1         ENDP
30: ;****FOR USE LATER****
31:               NOP
32:               NOP
33:               NOP
34:               NOP
35:               NOP
36:               NOP
37:               NOP
38: ;****PROC3****
39: PROC3         PROC     NEAR
40:               ADD      AX,BX        ;ALTER AX
41:               ADD      BX,CX        ;ALTER BX
42:               ADD      CX,CX        ;ALTER CX
43: RET
44: PROC3         ENDP
45: MY_CODE       ENDS
46: END           START
```

In the third section of the procedure, the data which was saved in the first section of the procedure is restored to its original location.

Finally, a RETurn is made to the main program in the manner described earlier by means of a RET instruction. As with the procedure CALL instruction,

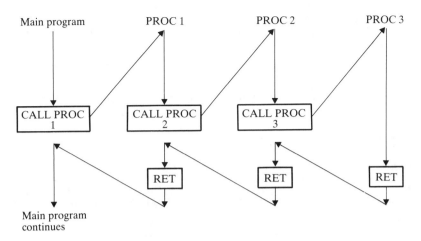

Figure 6.6 Nested procedures

Table 6.2 Values occurring in program of Listing 6.2

Content of the following	Before PROC1	Before POP AX	After PROC1	After PROC3
AX	1111	3333	1111	3333
BX	2222	2222	2222	6666
CX	4444	4444	4444	8888
RESULT_1	0000	3333	3333	3333
RESULT_2	0000	0000	0000	0000

there are two types of RETurn instruction, namely an intrasegment RETurn and an intersegment RETurn. In the case of an intrasegment return, two bytes are POPped off the stack and into the IP register to give the 16-bit offset within the code segment. When an intersegment return is made, four bytes are POPped off the stack; the first two are transferred to the CS register to form the base address of the code segment to which the return is made, and two bytes are transferred to the IP register to give the offset with the code segment. When the program is assembled, the assembler decides what type of RETurn is necessary from the type of CALL used to access the procedure.

Of the four sections in Fig. 6.5, only the second and final parts are mandatory. Since it is not always necessary to save the contents of all or even any of the registers on the stack, sections one and three of Fig. 6.5 are optional.

6.8 A program using a procedure

Listing 6.2 illustrates a program which CALLs a procedure containing all the sections in Fig. 6.5. The program initially loads registers AX, BX and CX with

```
 1: ;****NESTED PROCEDURES – LISTING 6.3****
26:              CALL      PROC2          ;CALL PROCEDURE PROC2
30: ;****PROC2****
31: PROC2    PROC      NEAR             ;PROCEDURE PROC2
32:          PUSH      BX               ;SAVE (BX) ON THE STACK
33:          ADD BX,CX                  ;ALTER BX
34:          MOV       RESULT_2,BX      ;SAVE (BX) IN RESULT_2
35:          POP       BX               ;RESTORE (BX)
36:          RET
37: PROC2    ENDP
```

Table 6.3   Values occurring in program of Listing 6.3

Content of the following	Before PROC1	Before CALL PROC2	After PROC2	After PROC1	After PROC3
AX	1111	3333	3333	1111	3333
BX	2222	2222	2222	2222	6666
CX	4444	4444	4444	4444	8888
RESULT_1	0000	3333	3333	3333	3333
RESULT_2	0000	0000	6666	6666	6666

the hex values 1111H, 2222H and 4444H, respectively, and CALLs procedure PROC1.

This procedure uses the AX register during its run-time, and it therefore saves the original data in AX on the stack in its first phase of operation (see program line 23). The main purpose of the procedure is to add the contents of register AX to BX, and to save the result in RESULT_1 in the data segment. Having done this, the original contents of AX are restored (see line 27), and then a RETurn is made to the main program.

After the program has executed the NOPs in lines 31–37, inclusive (which are to be replaced by instructions later), PROC3 is called. This procedure illustrates the effect on the registers of not saving the initial contents. The values listed in Table 6.2 appear in the computer at various points in the program.

6.9   Nested subroutines and procedures

Procedures are said to be *nested* when one procedure calls another, which may call yet another, and so on. The 'depth' to which procedures can be nested is limited only by the size of the stack. Figure 6.6 illustrates the general principle. Each time a procedure is called, the return address is pushed on the top of the stack. Thus, by the time that procedure PROC3 is being executed, three return addresses are stored on the stack; from PROC3, a return is made to the main program via PROC2 and PROC1.

A program illustrating the operation of nested procedures is given in Listing 6.3, and is a modification of Listing 6.2. The values in Table 6.3 are stored in the computer at various points during the run-time of the program.

7

Digital input and output

7.1 The I/O map of the 8086 and 8088

In addition to the 1 Mbyte of memory available to the 8086 and 8088 CPUs using memory mapping, a further 64 kbytes of addresses is also available for addressing I/O devices. (*Note:* not all 16-bit CPUs have these additional addresses.) The *I/O mapped I/O addressing map* of the 8086/88 chips is shown in Fig. 7.1. You will note that the addresses are in the range 0000H–FFFFH, i.e., they are 16-bit addresses rather than 20-bit addresses as used for memory mapping. Addresses in the range 00F8H–00FFH are reserved for Intel products, and should not be used when developing systems, otherwise clashes may occur with some Intel products.

Data can be 'read' or 'input' from a peripheral by the CPU by means of an IN (INput) instruction. An example of this is IN 42H, where 42H is the hexadecimal I/O mapped address of an 'input' port. Similarly, data can be as 'written' or 'output' to a peripheral by means of an OUT (OUTput) instruction such as OUT 40H (40H being the hex I/O mapped address of an output port).

In Intel terminology, a port may either be described as a fixed port or as a variable port. A *fixed port* is one having a 'fixed' address such as 40H or 0CAB3H. A *variable port* is one whose address is specified by the 16-bit value in register DX; the address that the data is to be transferred to (or from) can therefore be 'varied' by changing the contents of the DX register.

INPUT INSTRUCTIONS

An INput instruction is written in the form

IN accumulator,port

The instruction may transfer a byte or a word; if it is a byte, it is transferred to register AL, and if it is a word it is transferred to AX. Typical examples are

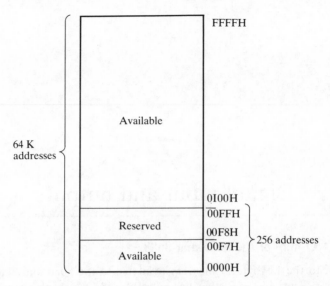

Figure 7.1 The addressing space for the system I/O.

```
IN AL,4DEH          ;typical 8-bit fixed port addressing
MOV DX,0ABCH        ;typical 16-bit variable port addressing
IN AX,DX
```

OUTPUT INSTRUCTIONS

An output instruction is written in the form

OUT port,accumulator

The instruction may transfer a byte or a word; if it is a byte, it is transferred from register AL, and if it is a word it is transferred from register AX. Examples are

```
OUT 42H,AL          ;8-bit fixed port addressing
MOV DX,0CBAH        ;16-bit variable port addressing
OUT DX,AL
```

7.2   A practical input/output port – the 8255

The basic concept of an I/O port was outlined in Chapter 2, and here we put flesh on the bones of the simple port by describing the 8255 Programmable Peripheral Interface (PPI).

This is a 40-pin dual-in-line package (DIP), large-scale integrated (LSI) chip designed to act as an interface between the CPU and peripherals. It can be programmed to operate in any one of several ways, and contains three 8-bit ports, referred to as port A, port B and port C. Moreover, port C can be programmed either as one 8-bit port or as two 4-bit ports; when used in the latter mode, port C can be used as a register which handles data transfer using electronic *handshaking*.

A block diagram of the 8255 PPI is illustrated in Fig. 7.2, where it is shown that the four high-order bits of port C can be combined with port A to give the 12-bit 'group A' configuration, and the low-order bits of port C can be combined with port B to give 'group B'.

We shall be using the port in a straightforward configuration in which either the CPU will read the state of switches connected either to port B or port C, or it will output data to either LEDs connected to port A. The reader is referred to the appropriate user guide for specialized applications.

The CPU is able to communicate independently with the three I/O ports within the 8255, and for this reason each is given its own 8-bit I/O mapped address; typical addresses may be

Port	Address (hex)
A	40
B	42
C	44

The following assembly language instructions illustrate the use of the port in a simple application:

```
PORTA     EQU     40H

PORTB     EQU     42H
  .
  .
  .

IN        AL,PORTB

OUT       PORTA,AL
  .
  .
  .
```

The first two lines use the EQU directive to specify the address of port A and port B, respectively. The third line causes the CPU to INput data from a peripheral connected to port B to register AL. The fourth line causes the data in register AL to be OUTput to a peripheral connected to port A. That is, the section of the program shown causes an automatic transfer of data from the peripheral connected to port B to the peripheral connected to port A.

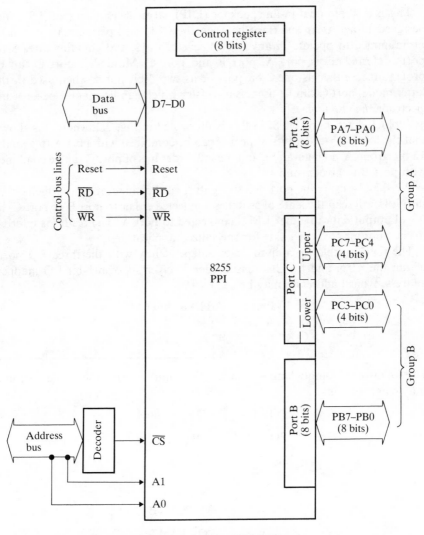

Figure 7.2 The 8255 PPI.

7.3 The control register of the 8255

The way in which the 8255 chip operates is specified by the data in the *control register* of the chip; it is the *responsibility of the programmer* to ensure that the chip is correctly initialized.

The control register has its own address which, in the following, is 46H. To send data to the control register, the program must include instructions similar to the following:

CONREG	EQU	46H
CONBYTE	EQU	8BH

.

.

.

MOV	AL,CONBYTE
OUT	CONREG,AL

.

The first line specifies the I/O mapped address of the control register, and the second sets up the data to be used in the control register. The third line MOVes 8BH (CONBYTE) into register AL (the meaning of the value 8BH is discussed later); the fourth line OUTputs the control byte to the control register.

The bit pattern for the control register is illustrated in Fig. 7.3. Bits D2, D5 and D6 are used for 'mode selection' purposes; we will restrict ourselves here to simple input and output applications, and we must transfer a logic '0' to each of these bits. The binary value transferred to bit D7 is the 'mode set' bit; for our

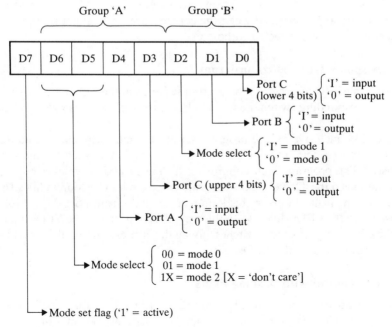

Figure 7.3 The bit pattern for the control register.

applications this must be logic '1'. Bits D0, D1, D3 and D4 are used to specify the operating state of the three ports; you must set these bits up to satisfy your own needs. In the case of the control byte (8BH) used in the above program, the PPI is set up as follows:

Bit	Value	Meaning
D7	1	Mode set flag is 'active'
D6	0	Group A in mode 0
D5	0	Group A in mode 0
D4	0	Port A = output port
D3	1	Port C (upper) = input port
D2	0	Group B in mode 0
D1	1	Port B = input port
D0	1	Port C (lower) = input port

7.4   A simple I/O module

The simple I/O module in Fig. 7.4 is used as a basic I/O peripheral which will allow us to develop a number of practical programs.

Eight LEDs, a_7–a_0, inclusive, are connected via buffer gates to port A of an 8255 chip; a logic '1' on any line from port A illuminates the LED connected to it, and a '0' extinguishes it. Eight switches, b_7–b_0, inclusive, are connected to port B; when the contacts of a switch are closed, a logic '0' is applied to its terminal, and a '1' is applied when the contacts are open. Eight more switches on the module are connected to port C.

7.5   A simple I/O control program

A program which enables you to control the LEDs in the I/O module by means of the corresponding switch, i.e., switch b_n controls LED a_n, is given in Listing 7.1.

Lines 3–5, inclusive, of the program set up the stack segment, the addresses of the 8255 registers and the control word being established by lines 9–13, inclusive. The program itself commences at line 14 and, after lines 14 and 15 have initialized the 8255 chip, the program enters an infinite loop in lines 16–19, inclusive. The instructions in this loop read the data from port B (line 16) and transfer it to the LEDs (line 17). In this way, the condition of the LEDs indicates via the CPU the state of the switches, giving the impression that the switches are directly connected to the LEDs.

7.6   I/O control with flashing lights

Listing 7.1 can easily be modified to cause any LED to flash on and off whenever the corresponding switch is in the logic '1' position. The modifications are shown in Listing 7.2.

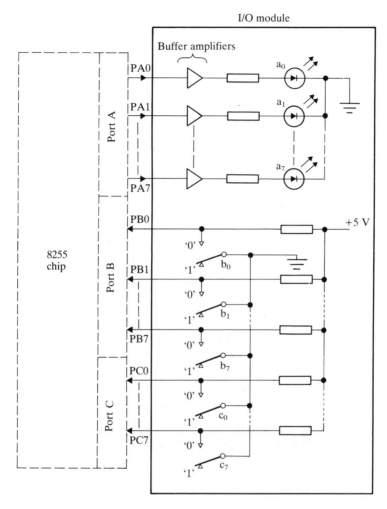

Figure 7.4 A simple I/O module (peripheral)

Line 18 of Listing 7.2 calls a LED 'flashing' procedure which resides in lines 21–36, inclusive of the program. This procedure has two effects. Firstly, it holds the existing LED display for a length of time specified by the contents of registers CX and DX (see lines 30 and 31). Secondly, it extinguishes the LEDs for the same length of time (see lines 23–25, inclusive).

Control is then returned to the main program, when the state of the switches are sampled once more. That is, the complete program including Listing 7.2 causes any LED corresponding to a switch which is in the logic '1' position to repeatedly flash on and off.

```
 1:  ;****LISTING 7.1 - SIMPLE I/O****
 2:  ;****STACK SEGMENT****
 3:  MY_STACK      SEGMENT    PARA       STACK
 4:                DB         100H       DUP(?)
 5:  MY_STACK      END
 6:  ;****CODE SEGMENT****
 7:  MY_CODE SEGMENT
 8:          ASSUME CS:MY_CODE,SS:MY_STACK
 9:  PORTA      EQU       40H
10:  PORTB      EQU       42H
11:  PORTC      EQU       44H
12:  CONREG     EQU       46H
13:  CONBYTE    EQU       8BH
14:  START:  MOV   AL,CONBYTE           ;INITIALIZE 8255 I/O PORT
15:          OUT   CONREG,AL
16:  INPUT:  IN    AL,PORTB             ;READ STATE OF SWITCHES ON MODULE
17:          OUT   PORTA,AL             ;OUTPUT DATA TO LEDs
18:          NOP                        ;FOR FUTURE USE
19:          JMP   INPUT                ;GET NEW DATA
20:  MY_CODE ENDS
21:  END     START
```

```
 1: ;****LISTING 7.2 – I/O WITH FLASHING LIGHTS****
18:                CALL       FLASH       ;CALL FLASHING LED ROUTINE
19:                JMP        INPUT       ;GET NEW DATA
20: ;****FLASHING LED PROCEDURE****
21: FLASH          PROC
22:                CALL       DELAY
23:                XOR        AL,AL
24:                OUT        PORTA,AL
25:                CALL       DELAY
26:                RET
27: FLASH          ENDP
28: ;;;;;;;;;;;;
29: DELAY          PROC
30:                MOV        CX,10H
31: LONG:          MOV        DX,200DH
32: TEST:          DEC        DX
33:                JNZ        TEST
34:                LOOP       LONG
35:                RET
36: DELAY          ENDP
37: MY_CODE        ENDS
38: END            START
```

7.7   Using an I/O port for code conversion

Many commercial and industrial systems need to convert one type of code to
another. For example, in an industrial control system, the angular displacement
or movement of the output shaft of the system may be measured by a transducer
whose output is in a special binary code known as the Gray code (after its
inventor). The reader is referred to specialized texts (see References for further
study) for the reason why this code is used.

Unfortunately, this code is not amenable to normal arithmetic processes, and
each value must be converted into its pure binary version before arithmetic
operations can be performed on it. The relationship between the 4-bit Gray code
and the 4-bit pure binary code is given in Table 7.1. (Strictly speaking, the Gray
code can have any number of bits in it, but we restrict the discussion here to a
4-bit code for purely practical purposes.)

In this section of the book we concentrate on developing a simple program
which converts the 4-bit Gray code into the 4-bit pure binary code. We consider
later an application of the conversion process.

Suppose that the 4-bit Gray code is input to the computer via port B of the
I/O module as shown in Fig. 7.5, and that the pure binary version is output to
the LEDs connected to port A. The program which performs the code conversion
is shown in Listing 7.3. You will notice that the code conversion procedure, lines
34–38, inclusive, is written as a subroutine; this enables you to use the procedure
in other programs.

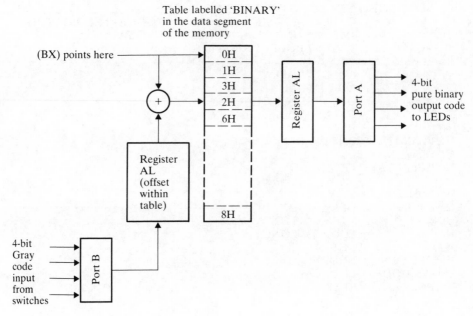

Figure 7.5 Using the XLAT instruction to convert a Gray code value to its pure binary equivalent.

Table 7.1 4-bit Gray code and pure binary code

Gray code (input)		Pure binary code (output)	
binary	hex	binary	hex
0000	0	0000	0
0001	1	0001	1
0011	3	0010	2
0010	2	0011	3
0110	6	0100	4
0111	7	0101	5
0101	5	0110	6
0100	4	0111	7
1100	C	1000	8
1101	D	1001	9
1111	F	1010	A
1110	E	1011	B
1010	A	1100	C
1011	B	1101	D
1001	9	1110	E
1000	8	1111	F

```
 1: ;****LISTING 7.3 – CODE CONVERSION USING I/O****
 2: ;****STACK SEGMENT****
 3: MY_STACK        SEGMENT     PARA    STACK
 4:                 DB          100H    DUP(?)
 5: MY_STACK        ENDS
 6: ;****DATA SEGMENT****
 7: MY_DATA SEGMENT
 8: BINARY          DB          0H,1H,3H,2H,7H,6H,4H,5H,0FH,0EH,0CH,0DH,8H,9H,0BH,0AH
 9: MY_DATA ENDS
10: ;****CODE SEGMENT****
11: MY_CODE SEGMENT
12:         ASSUME CS:MY_CODE,SS:MY_STACK,DS:MY_DATA
13: PORTA           EQU         40H
14: PORTB           EQU         42H
15: PORTC           EQU         44H
16: CONREG          EQU         46H
17: CONBYTE         EQU         8BH
18: START:  MOV     AX,MY_DATA          ;INITIALIZE DATA SEGMENT
19:         MOV     DS,AX
20:         MOV     BX,OFFSET BINARY    ;PUT STARTING ADDRESS OF BINARY
21:                                     ;TABLE INTO BX. EQUIVALENT TO
22:                                     ;THE INSTRUCTION LEA BX,BINARY
23:         MOV     AL,CONBYTE          ;INITIALIZE 8255 I/O PORT
24:         OUT     CONREG,AL
25: INPUT:  IN      AL,PORTB            ;GET GRAY CODE
26:         CALL    CONVERT             ;CONVERT IT TO BINARY
27:         NOP                         ;NOPs FOR FUTURE USE
28:         NOP
29:         NOP
30:         NOP
31:         OUT     PORTA,AL            ;DISPLAY BINARY VALUE ON LEDs
32:         JMP     INPUT               ;GET NEW DATA
33: ;****CODE CONVERSION****
34: CONVERT PROC
35:         AND     AL,0FH              ;MASK OUT NON-SIGNIFICANT BITS
36:         XLAT    BINARY              ;TRANSLATE INTO BINARY
37:         RET
38: CONVERT ENDP
39: MY_CODE ENDS
40:         END     START
```

The conversion code labelled BINARY (see line 8) is stored in the data segment, and values in the code are accessed by the XLAT (transLATe) instruction as shown in Fig. 7.5; the XLAT instruction implements the *lookup table* in line 8 as follows.

The CPU calculates the offset between the beginning of the data segment and the first item in the conversion code, and the instruction in line 20 loads this value into register BX. In effect, register BX stores the effective address of the starting point of the table labelled BINARY.

The instruction in line 25 inputs the 4-bit Gray code from the switches connected to port B to the AL register. In line 26, control is transferred to the code conversion procedure CONVERT – also see line 34 – where the four most significant bits of the AL register are masked out (in fact, these represent electronic 'garbage' and are useless). The XLAT instruction (line 36) uses the contents of register AL (the Gray code) as an offset within the table (BINARY) to determine the required binary value.

If, for example, the Gray code value is 0011 (3H), the required output is determined from the lookup table (see also Table 7.1 and Fig. 7.5) as 2H; immediately before the XLAT instruction the content of the AL register is 03H (the Gray code value), and afterwards it is 02H (the pure binary equivalent value). After a return is made to the main program, the value in the AL register (02H in this case) is output to the LEDs – see line 31. In this way, the Gray code which is input to the CPU via port B is converted into pure binary and is output on the LEDs connected to port A. The program repeats the process continuously, so that any change in the Gray code is displayed as its equivalent binary code on the LEDs.

7.8   Digital control of an electro-mechanical control system

A simple version of a *remote position control system* using the code conversion technique described in Section 7.7 is shown in Fig. 7.6. The angular motion of the output shaft of the system is measured using a transducer giving a 4-bit Gray code output, which is applied to the computer via port B. (Since the angular accuracy of a 4-bit encoder is only 22.5°, a practical encoder would use more than four bits to give greater accuracy.) The *reference signal* corresponding to the required angular position of the output shaft is input to the computer via port C. The computer must perform two operations, as follows:

1. It converts the Gray code into pure binary (which we shall call code Y).
2. It subtracts code Y from the binary reference signal (which we shall call code X).

The binary difference $(X - Y)$ is described as the binary *error signal*. The error signal is amplified by the system controller and is used to drive the motor, causing the output shaft to rotate. The net result is that the output shaft is

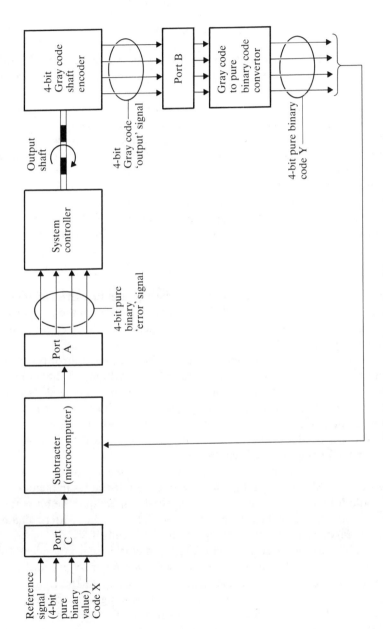

Figure 7.6 The basis of a digital control system.

```
 1:   ;****LISTING 7.4 – POSITION CONTROL SYSTEM ERROR DETECTOR****
27:      MOV   AH,AL      ;SAVE CODE Y IN AH
28:      IN    AL,PORTC   ;READ "REFERENCE" SIGNAL (CODE X)
29:      AND   AL,0FH     ;MASK OUT NON-SIGNIFICANT BITS
30:      SUB   AL,AH      ;CALCULATE BINARY ERROR = CODE X – CODE Y
```

ultimately aligned with the position demanded by the reference signal, so that the error signal is reduced to zero. At this point in time, torque is no longer applied to the motor shaft, and it becomes stationary.

We will concern ourselves here only with the part of the system which evaluates and displays the digital error signal. If you load Listing 7.3 into the computer and modify the lines shown in Listing 7.4, the computer will evaluate and display, on the LEDs connected to port A, the pure binary error signal which exists between the reference signal and the pure binary version of the Gray code output signal.

It should be pointed out that the program is only intended to illustrate the general principle involved in digital error detection, and further program modifications are needed before it can be used with a practical system.

7.9   Stepper motor control

A *stepper control* is a d.c. motor whose output shaft rotates in a series of angular 'steps' under *direct digital control* (DDC). Readers interested in the principal of operation of this type of motor should refer to specialized texts (see References for further study).

A simplified diagram of a system which can be used to control a 4-phase stepper motor is shown in Fig. 7.7. The 'stator', or fixed part of the motor, is energized from port A via 'buffer' amplifiers; a buffer amplifier is needed in each stator line to provide the current needed by the motor. The bit pattern applied to the stator causes the rotor to 'lock' into a particular position; any variation in the bit pattern results in the rotor moving one step at a time in either the clockwise or the anticlockwise direction.

Additionally, a 'direction' switch, D, mounted on the motor equipment is connected to port B; if the signal from D = 0, the shaft rotates in a clockwise direction, and if D = 1 it rotates in an anticlockwise direction. The bit pattern changes that are necessary are given in Table 7.2; each bit pattern change produces an angular step in the shaft position of typically 1.8°.

The initial bit pattern for both anticlockwise and clockwise rotation is 0110B (or 06H). This pattern is 'rotated' to the left by the computer to give anticlockwise rotation of the rotor (see Table 7.2), and is rotated to the right in the computer to give clockwise rotation of the shaft. Depending on the design of the motor there may be, say, 200 mechanical steps to produce one complete revolution of the shaft. To produce 'continuous' rotation, it is simply a matter of continuously 'rotating' the data in the computer and outputting it to the stepper

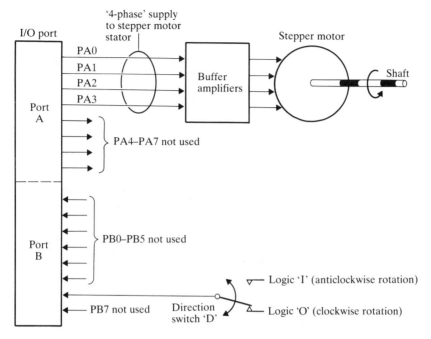

Figure 7.7   Direct digital control of a stepper motor.

Table 7.2   Bit pattern changes

Clockwise rotation of rotor					Anticlockwise rotation of rotor			
Logic level applied to the lines					Logic signal applied to the lines			
PA3	PA2	PA1	PA0		PA3	PA2	PA1	PA0
Initial data 0	1	1	0	Initial data 0	1	1	0
1st step 0	0	1	1	1st step 1	1	0	0
2nd step 1	0	0	1	2nd step 1	0	0	1
3rd step 1	1	0	0	3rd step 0	0	1	1
4th (1st) step 0	1	1	0	4th (1st) step 0	1	1	0

motor at each stage. The speed of rotation of the motor shaft is controlled by the time delay between OUTput instructions.

However, you will note from Table 7.2 that the data word is only four bits in length. This is handled in the 8088 by using an initial 8-bit pattern of 01100110B (or 66H). When this is rotated right (for clockwise rotation of the rotor) using an ROR instruction, the bit pattern in Table 7.2 is produced. Similarly, anticlockwise rotation of the shaft occurs when the 8-bit pattern is rotated left using an ROL instruction.

```
 1:  ;****LISTING 7.5 – STEPPER MOTOR CONTROL****
 2:  ;****STACK SEGMENT****
 3:  MY_STACK     SEGMENT   PARA              STACK
 4:               DB        100H    DUP(?)
 5:  MY_STACK     ENDS
 6:  ;****CODE SEGMENT****
 7:  MY_CODE  SEGMENT
 8:           ASSUME  CS:MY_CODE,SS:MY_STACK
 9:  PORTA    EQU     40H
10:  PORTB    EQU     42H
11:  PORTC    EQU     44H
12:  CONREG   EQU     46H
13:  CONBYTE  EQU     8BH
14:  START:   MOV     AL,CONBYTE    ;INITIALIZE 8255 I/O PORT
15:           OUT     CONREG,AL
16:           MOV     AH,AL         ;INITIALIZE STEPPER MOTOR DATA
17:  STEP:    MOV     AH,AL         ;SAVE COPY OF BINARY PATTERN IN AH
18:           OUT     PORTA,AL      ;OUTPUT DATA TO STEPPER MOTOR
19:           CALL    DELAY         ;AND HOLD IT THERE
20:           IN      AL,PORTB      ;SAMPLE STATE OF DIRECTION SWITCH
21:           AND     AL,40H
22:           JNZ     ANTI          ;IF D=1, ANTICLOCKWISE ROTATION
23:           MOV     AL,AH         ;OTHERWISE GET COPY OF ROTATION DATA
24:           ROR     AL,1          ;AND ROTATE SHAFT CLOCKWISE
25:           JMP     STEP          ;TAKE NEXT STEP
26:  ANTI:    MOV     AL,AH         ;GET COPY OF ROTATION DATA
27:           ROL     AL,1          ;AND ROTATE SHAFT ANTICLOCKWISE
28:           JMP     STEP          ;TAKE NEXT STEP
29:  ;****TIME DELAY PROGRAM****
30:  DELAY    PROC
31:           MOV     CX,1H
32:  LONG:    MOV     DX,2000H
33:  TEST:    DEC     DX
34:           JNZ     TEST
35:           LOOP    LONG
36:           RET
37:  DELAY    ENDP
38:  MY_CODE  ENDS
39:           END     START
```

A program which gives control of the stepper motor is obtained by entering the program in Listing 7.5; the program lines 1–15, inclusive, simply establish the addresses and working conditions of the I/O port.

Line 16 sets up the binary pattern 01100110 (described above) in register AL. The program proper commences in line 17, at which point the stepper motor data is 'saved' in register AH. The data is then output to the motor in line 18, after which the program calls for a time delay. This time delay is the means used to control the speed of the motor. If you vary the value stored in registers CX and DX (see lines 31 and 32), you will vary the time delay between steps; a net reduction in the value stored in the registers reduces the time delay and increases the speed of rotation. As you will see, no method is provided to alter the shaft speed (other than by altering the program instructions); you will find it an interesting exercise to modify the program so that you can use switches connected to, say, PB3–PB0 as an 'electronic gearbox' to give speed ratios from 1:1 to 15:1 (or 16:1 with a little care).

In lines 20–22, inclusive, the state of the 'D' switch is monitored and, depending on the logic level it provides, the stepper motor shaft rotates either anticlockwise or clockwise. At the end of each step (either at line 25 or line 28), control is transferred back to line 17 to enable the next rotational step to occur.

There is no provision for a 'stop' button in this system; this can be provided either by using a 'stop' switch connected to port B (which is sampled during each pass of the loop), or by using the interrupt facilities of the CPU (see Chapter 9).

7.10   A pneumatic ram control system

The majority of industrial systems using mechanical rams use either a pneumatic or a hydraulic power source. Whilst the study of the sequencing of ram mechanisms for control systems such as automatic packaging plant would warrant a complete book, it is not out of place here to introduce the concept of a simple ram control mechanism.

Consider the simple ram control arrangement in Fig. 7.8 (this can, of course, be simulated using the I/O module described earlier). The signals from lines PA0 and PA1 of port A are used to control the flow of compressed air to opposite ends of the pneumatic ram. Line PB0 of port B is connected to the 'start' push button, and lines PB1 and PB2 are respectively connected to sensors which detect when the ram is at the start of the stroke (SOS) or at the end of the stroke (EOS). A logic '1' level at the 8255 I/O chip lines represent the following:

PA0 – admit air to drive the ram outwards (forwards)
PA1 – admit air to return the ram to the start position
PB0 – start the outward stroke of the ram
PB1 – ram at the start of the stroke (SOS)
PB2 – ram at the end of the stroke (EOS)

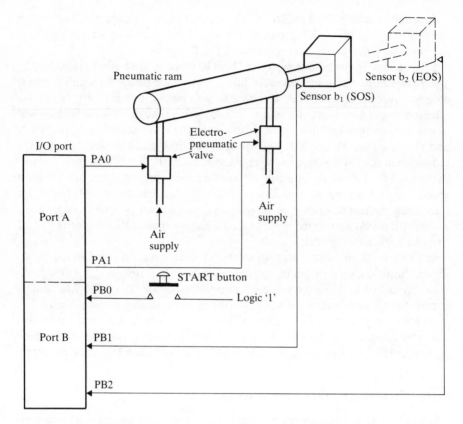

Figure 7.8 A simple pneumatic ram controller.

Table 7.3 Logic levels during stroke

	Input signals			Output signals		Comment
	PB2	PB1	PB0	PA1	PA0	
Ram stationary	0	1	0	0	0	
Press START button	0	1	1	0	1	Commence cycle
Release Start button	0	1	0	0	1	
During outward stroke	0	0	0	0	1	
End of outward stroke	1	0	0	1	0	Ram fully extended
During return stroke	0	0	0	1	0	
End of return stroke (end of sequence)	0	1	0	0	0	Ram stationary

```
 1: ;****LISTING 7.6 – SIMPLE PNEUMATIC RAM CONTROL****
 2: ;****STACK SEGMENT****
 3: MY_STACK        SEGMENT  PARA      STACK
 4:                 DB       100H      DUP(?)
 5: MY_STACK        ENDS
 6: ;****CODE SEGMENT****
 7: MY_CODE         SEGMENT
 8:                 ASSUME CS:MY_CODE,SS:MY_STACK
 9:        PORTA         EQU     40H
10:        PORTB         EQU     42H
11:        PORTC         EQU     44H
12:        CONREG        EQU     46H
13:        CONBYTE       EQU     8BH
14: START:        MOV     AL,CONBYTE
15:               OUT     CONREG,AL                ;INITIALIZE 8255 I/O PORT
16:        S_BUT         EQU     1H
17:        F_STROKE      EQU     1H
18:        F_COMP        EQU     4H
19:        R_STROKE      EQU     2H
20:        R_COMP        EQU     2H
21:        STOP          EQU     0H
22: BEGIN:        IN      AL,PORTB                 ;READ SYSTEM DATA
23:               AND     AL,S_BUT                 ;HAS 'START' BUTTON BEEN PRESSED
24:               JZ      BEGIN                    ;IF NOT, CHECK AGAIN
25:               MOV     AL,F_STROKE              ;COMMENCE FORWARD STROKE
26:               OUT     PORTA,AL
27: EOS:          IN      AL,PORTB                 ;IS FORWARD STROKE COMPLETE?
28:               AND     AL,F_COMP
29:               JZ      EOS                      ;IF NOT, CHECK AGAIN
30:               MOV     AL,R_STROKE              ;COMMENCE REVERSE STROKE
31:               OUT     PORTA,AL
32: SOS:          IN      AL,PORTB                 ;IS REVERSE STROKE COMPLETE?
33:               AND     AL,R_COMP
34:               JZ      SOS                      ;IF NOT CHECK AGAIN
35:               MOV     AL,STOP                  ;SEQUENCE COMPLETE, STOP DRIVE
36:               OUT     PORTA,AL
37:               JMP     BEGIN                    ;CHECK IF 'START' BUTTON HAS BEEN PRESSED
38: MY_CODE ENDS
39: END           START
```

The logic levels at various points during the stroke are shown in Table 7.3. The ram cycle is initiated by pressing the 'start' button, and the complete cycle is simply an outward (forward) stroke followed by a return stroke. On completion of the cycle, the ram remains stationary until the 'start' button is pressed once more.

As with the stepper motor program, no 'stop' button is provided; you may like to add this feature using either an additional switch connected to port B or the interrupt facilities of the CPU.

The program which controls the system is shown in Listing 7.6. As before, lines 1–15, inclusive, initialize the stack and I/O port so that port A is an output port, and ports B and C are input ports (the latter not being used in this program). Lines 16–21, inclusive, of Listing 7.6 set up data to be used in the program as follows:

S_BUT corresponds to the start button being pressed
F_STROKE corresponds to the forward stroke signal at PA0
F_COMP corresponds to the completion of the forward stroke
R_STROKE corresponds to the return stroke signal at PA1
R_COMP corresponds to the completion of the return stroke
STOP corresponds to air being cut off to both ends of the ram.

Lines 22–24, inclusive, of Listing 7.6 contain a loop which waits for the 'start' button to be pressed. When the button is pressed, the forward or outward stroke is initiated (see lines 25 and 26); following this, the instructions in lines 27–29, inclusive, continuously test to see if the end of the outward stroke (EOS) has been reached. When this occurs, the return stroke is initiated (see lines 30 and 31); following this, program lines 32–34 continuously test to see if the ram is fully retracted (SOS).

When SOS is reached the cycle is complete, lines 35 and 36 output logic 0s to PA0 and PA1 to shut off the air supply to both ends of the ram. Finally, line 37 transfers control to line 22, where the computer waits for the 'start' button to be pressed once more.

8

Analogue output and input

8.1 A digital-to-analogue convertor (DAC)

Since a digital computer performs calculations in binary, its output is available only in this form. In the 'real world', results are often needed in *analogue* form, that is, the signal (an electrical voltage) must vary smoothly as the digital equivalent varies.

A digital signal can be converted into an analogue signal by means of a *digital-to-analogue convertor* (DAC). Many forms of integrated circuit (IC) DAC are available, the basis of one form being shown in Fig. 8.1. This is known as a *weighted resistor DAC*, and contains a number of resistors having a resistance which is 'weighted' in inverse binary order to the 'number' of the data bus line to which it is connected. That is, the resistor connected to the most significant data bus line (line D7) has the lowest resistance, and the resistor in the least significant data bus line (line D0) has the highest resistance.

Consequently, when a logic '1' is applied to data bus line D7, it causes a current to flow in that line which is 128 times greater than the current which flows in the resistor connected to data bus line D0 when it has a logic '1' applied to it. The currents in all the resistors are added together at junction J, and the current, I, flowing in resistor R_0 is the sum of the currents in all the resistors. That is,

$$I = I_0 + I_1 + I_2 + I_3 + I_4 + I_5 + I_6 + I_7$$

Consequently, the voltage V_0 which appears across resistor R_0 represents the analogue equivalent of the byte applied to the data bus.

If a logic '1' is applied to line D0 of Fig. 8.1, i.e., the binary word 01H is on the data bus, and the DAC produces an output of 1 mV, then a byte of 02H on the bus produces 2 mV, etc. The maximum analogue voltage output of 255 mV is produced when the hex value FFH is applied to the data bus.

The DAC circuit in Fig. 8.1 is capable of producing only a 'positive' output voltage. If both positive and negative output voltages are needed, an alternative

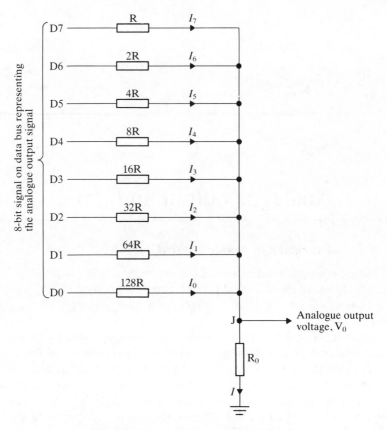

Figure 8.1 A weighted-resistor DAC.

design of DAC circuit is needed. The reader is referred to other specialist texts for further information on these designs (see Reference 9 in References for further study).

Whilst the circuit design of some DACs differs from that in Fig. 8.1, the circuit illustrates the general principle of the DAC. DACs capable of handling a digital input of 16 bits and more are commercially available.

8.2   Using a DAC as a microprocessor-based waveform generator

Since the computer can generate any binary pattern, and the binary pattern can be converted to a voltage by a DAC, a computer and a DAC can be combined to produce any form of electrical voltage waveform. There are, however, practical limitations to this combination.

One limit is that there is a lower value to the time between the changes in the binary value which produces the analogue voltage. This limit is set not only by

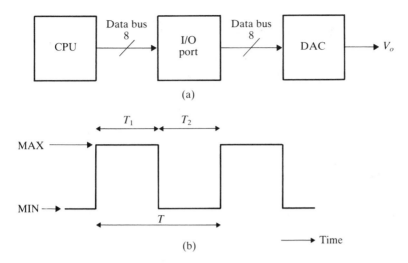

Figure 8.2 A rectangular waveform generator.

the clock frequency of the CPU but also by the number of instructions that have to be executed between each change in output voltage. In turn, this restricts the maximum frequency of the waveform from the DAC.

8.3 A rectangular waveform generator

The basis of a waveform generator is shown in Fig. 8.2(a). A program which produces the rectangular output waveform in Fig. 8.2(b) from an 8-bit DAC is given in Listing 8.1. This listing is the basis of other programs in this chapter, and you should retain the line numbering when entering the program into the computer.

The variables MIN and MAX, specified as zero and FFH, are used by the program to give the digital value of the MINimum and the MAXimum value of the waveform (see Fig. 8.2(b)). The period of time T_1 (also known as the 'mark' period of the wave) and T_2 (known as the 'space' period) are controlled by a time delay in the program. The total time, T, taken to complete one cycle is known as the *periodic time* of the wave, and the frequency, f, is given by $f = 1/T$ Hz, where T is in seconds.

The DAC is assumed to be connected to port A of an 8255 PPI, and the early instructions in the program establish port A as an output port (the mode of operation of the other ports does not matter in this application).

The main program commences at the label WAVE, where MAX (= FFH) is output to the DAC, and is maintained there for a period of time set by the time delay program. This establishes the 'mark' period of the waveform. Next, MIN (= 0) is output to the DAC, and is maintained there for the same period of time.

```
 1: ;****DAC APPLICATION – RECTANGULAR WAVE – LISTING 8.1****
 2: ;****STACK SEGMENT****
 3: MY_STACK        SEGMENT PARA   STACK
 4:            DB   100H     DUP(?)
 5: MY_STACK        ENDS
 6:                                ;FOR USE LATER
 7: ;
 8: ;
 9: ;
10: ;****CODE SEGMENT****
11: MY_CODE SEGMENT
12: PORTA      EQU  40H
13: PORTB      EQU  42H
14: PORTC      EQU  44H
15: CONREG     EQU  46H
16: CONBYTE    EQU  82H
17: MIN        EQU  0
18: MAX        EQU  0FFH
19:            ASSUME SS:MY_STACK,CS:MY_CODE
20: START:     MOV  AL,CONBYTE    ;INITIALIZE 8255 PPI
21:            OUT  CONREG,AL
22: WAVE:      MOV  AL,MAX        ;GET MAXIMUM OUTPUT
23:            OUT  PORTA,AL      ;OUTPUT IT TO DAC
24:            CALL DELAY         ;AND HOLD IT THERE (MARK PERIOD)
25:            MOV  AL,MIN        ;GET MINIMUM OUTPUT
26:            OUT  PORTA,AL      ;OUTPUT IT TO DAC
27:            CALL DELAY         ;AND HOLD IT THERE (SPACE PERIOD)
28:            JMP  WAVE          ;REPEAT WAVE
29: ;                             ;FOR USE LATER
30: ;
31: ;
32: ;
33: ;
34: ;
35: ;
36: ;****TIME DELAY****
37: DELAY      PROC NEAR
38:            MOV  CX,10H
39: LONG:      MOV  DX,2000H
40: TEST:      DEC  DX
41:            JNZ  TEST
42:            LOOP LONG
43:            RET
44: DELAY      ENDP
45: MY_CODE ENDS
46: END        START
```

This establishes the 'space' period of the wave. This process is repeated continuously, to give the square wave output in Fig. 8.2(b).

In the case of Listing 8.1, the time delay is fairly long, giving a low output frequency. The frequency is increased by reducing the value stored in the

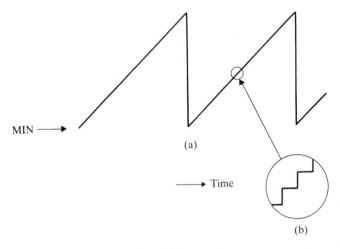

Figure 8.3 A run-up sawtooth wave.

registers CX and DX; the highest frequency that can be obtained by the program is produced by removing both of the CALL DELAY instructions.

Several variations of the program are possible, including changing the value of MAX and MIN to give a waveform of different amplitude, and also changing the time periods T_1 and T_2 relative to one another to alter the mark-to-space ratio for the wave.

8.4 A 'ramp' or 'sawtooth' waveform generator

A typical 'run-up' sawtooth waveform, as may be associated with the time base of a cathode-ray oscilloscope, is shown in Fig. 8.3(a). The waveform can be produced using a DAC simply by commencing at some digital value MIN, and incrementing the value one bit at a time; when the incremented value is output to the DAC, it is converted into the run-up ramp waveform. The output from the DAC increases in a series of steps (see inset (b)), each step in voltage corresponding to a change in the least significant bit in the binary word.

Listing 8.2 shows the modifications needed to Listing 8.1 in order to generate the run-up waveform from the DAC. In this case, the value MIN is zero; this value is continuously incremented, eventually reaching the count of FFH to give the maximum output voltage. The next incrementing step causes a value of (1 + FF) = 00H to be output to the DAC, resulting in the output from the DAC falling to zero again, causing the sawtooth wave to be repetitive.

As with the square wave, the time delay between steps is controlled by the value in registers CX and DX; this provides a means of controlling the repetition rate of the waveform. The highest frequency is obtained by removing the CALL delay instruction from the program.

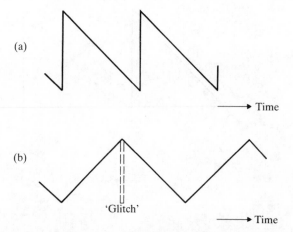

Figure 8.4   (a) A run-down sawtooth wave; (b) a triangular wave.

```
1: ;****DAC APPLICATION – SAWTOOTH WAVE – LISTING 8.2****
22:              MOV      AL,MIN      ;GET MINIMUM OUTPUT
23: RAMP_UP:     OUT      PORTA,AL    ;OUTPUT IT TO DAC
24:              CALL     DELAY       ;AND HOLD IT THERE
25:              INC      AL          ;INCREMENT DATA
26:              JMP      RAMP_UP     ;AND OUTPUT IT TO DAC
27:
28:
```

The program can be modified in a number of ways. For example, the amplitude of the waveform can be altered so that it commences at a non-zero value, and can be arranged to terminate at some value other than FFH. The program can also be altered to give the run-down sawtooth waveform in Fig. 8.4(a), or to give the triangular wave in Fig. 8.4(b). In the latter case, you must be careful to ensure that your program does not produce a sudden transition or 'glitch' at the peak of the wave.

8.5   Generating a waveform using a lookup table

Waveforms which are defined by a mathematical function, such as a sine wave, can be difficult to program, and an easy method of dealing with them is to use a lookup table. This technique is illustrated in Listing 8.3 which, once more, is an edited version of Listing 8.1.

The program begins by loading the effective address (LEA) of the first item of data in the TABLE into register BX, and follows this by 'clearing' the table pointer counter AL by MOVing zero into it. It is next necessary to save AL on the stack by means of a PUSH AX instruction; the reason is that the translate (XLAT) instruction uses AL to store an item of data from the translation table.

```
 1: ;****WAVEFORM GENERATOR USING A LOOKUP TABLE – LISTING 8.3****
 6: ;****DATA SEGMENT****
 7: MY_DATA SEGMENT
 8: TABLE     DB   18H,0H,28H,4FH,60H,50H,40H,0B0H,0B0H,0C0H,0D0H,0C0H,0F0H,0FFH
 9: MY_DATA ENDS
17: ;
18: ;
19:        ASSUME SS:MY_STACK,CS:MY_CODE,DS:MY_DATA
20: START:  MOV    AL,CONBYTE
21:         OUT    CONREG,AL       ;INITIALIZE 8255 PPI
22:         LEA    BX,TABLE
23: BEGIN:  MOV    AL,0H           ;GET ADDRESS OF TABLE
24: WAVE:   PUSH   AX              ;CLEAR AL (TABLE COUNTER)
25:         XLAT   TABLE           ;SAVE TABLE COUNTER VALUE
26:         OUT    PORTA,AL        ;GET DATA FROM TABLE
27:         CALL   DELAY           ;OUTPUT IT TO DAC
28:         POP    AX              ;AND HOLD IT THERE
29:         INC    AL              ;RESTORE TABLE COUNTER VALUE
30:         CMP    AL,0EH          ;INCREMENT TABLE COUNTER
31:         JZ     BEGIN           ;TABLE FINISHED?
32:         JMP    WAVE            ;IF SO, BEGIN AGAIN
                                   ;IF NOT, CONTINUE WITH WAVE
```

When the data has been extracted from the TABLE, it is output to the DAC and is held there for a period of time set by the DELAY procedure.

The table counter is then restored by the POP AX instruction, after which the counter is incremented in preparation for fetching the next item of data from the table.

Having sampled an item of data from the table and prepared itself to fetch another, the CPU checks whether it has scanned through the complete table. It does so by CoMParing the value in the table counter with $(n + 1)$, where n is the number of values in the table. Since there are 14 items of data in the TABLE, the final one is 'number' 13 (remember, the first item is 'number' zero!), the CMP 0EH instruction tests for the 'end' condition and sets the flags accordingly.

If not every value in the table has been accessed, the CMP 0EH instruction clears the ZF and the JZ BEGIN instruction is ignored. The CPU then executes the JMP WAVE instruction, and fetches and outputs the next value in the table. After the final item in the table has been output to the DAC, the table pointer register contains 0EH, and the JZ BEGIN instruction is obeyed. This has the effect of resetting the table counter to zero, and the whole process is repeated again; in this way the program generates the repetitive waveform in Fig. 8.5.

The shape of the waveform generated can be altered by modifying the data stored in the TABLE; it is then necessary only to change the VALUE in the CMP AL,table_length instruction in line 30 to agree with the new table length.

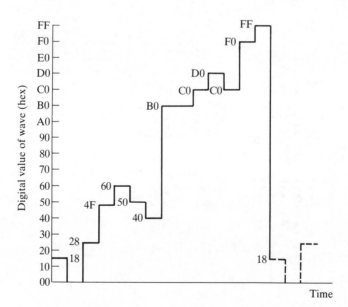

Figure 8.5   Waveform produced by Listing 8.3.

The frequency of the waveform can be altered by modifying the parameters in the DELAY procedure in the manner outlined earlier.

8.6 A software-driven analogue-to-digital convertor (ADC)

Many variables in the 'real world' such as temperature, barometric pressure, etc., are measured with analogue sensors or transducers. Electronic circuits known as *analogue-to-digital convertors* (ADC) are used to convert the analogue signal to the equivalent digital signal, so that the digital signal can be processed by a computer. Many sophisticated ADCs are commercially available, and we limit the treatment here to an ADC which is related to the earlier work on DACs.

A simple *continuous-balance ADC* is shown in Fig. 8.6. An unknown value of analogue voltage, V_u, is compared in an electronic comparator amplifier with the output voltage, V_0, from the DAC section (which is identical to the DAC described earlier) of the ADC. The program in Listing 8.4 (which is a modification of Listing 8.3) controls the ADC, and is described in the following.

The program initially causes the CPU to output 00H to the DAC (see line 23), which responds by producing zero volts. This value is compared with V_u in an electronic comparator (see Fig. 8.6) and, since V_u is finite, the comparator gives an output of logic '1' to indicate that $V_u > V_0$. (*Note:* Some comparators give an output of logic '0' under this condition; if you have one which does this, you will need to modify the program to account for this fact.) The output from the comparator is fed back to pin PB6 of port B of the I/O port.

The CPU reads the state of port B (see line 25) and tests the logic level on line PB6. Since it finds that $V_u > V_0$, it increments the data applied to the DAC (see

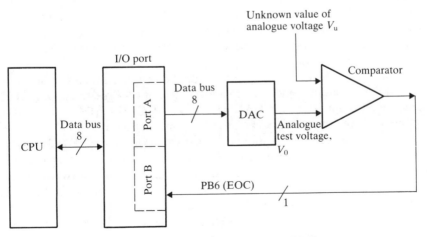

Figure 8.6 A continuous-balance ADC

```
 1:  ;****CONTINUOUS BALANCE ADC – LISTING 8.4****
 8:  RESULT    DB    (0H)
17:  MIN       EQU   0
18:  EOC       EQU   40H          ;TEST PATTERN FOR END OF CONVERSION
19:            ASSUME DS:MY_DATA,SS:MY_STACK,CS:MY_CODE
20:  START:    MOV   AL,CONBYTE   ;INITIALIZE 8255 PPI
21:            OUT   CONREG,AL
22:  CONVERT:  MOV   AL,MIN       ;GET MINIMUM OUTPUT
23:  RAMP_UP:  OUT   PORTA,AL     ;OUTPUT IT TO DAC SECTION OF ADC
24:            PUSH  AX           ;SAVE TEST DATA
25:            IN    AL,PORTB     ;READ COMPARATOR OUTPUT
26:            AND   AL,EOC       ;END OF CONVERSION YET?
27:            JNZ   CONTINUE     ;IF NOT, CONTINUE TESTING
28:            POP   AX           ;GET TEST DATA FROM STACK
29:            MOV   RESULT,AL    ;AND SAVE IT IN 'RESULT'
30:            OUT   PORTA,AL     ;AND DISPLAY IT ON THE LEDs
31:            CALL  DELAY        ;HOLD THE DISPLAY FOR A TIME
32:            JMP   CONVERT      ;BEGIN CONVERSION AGAIN
33:  CONTINUE: POP   AX           ;RESTORE TEST DATA
34:            INC   AL           ;INCREMENT TEST DATA
35:            JMP   RAMP_UP      ;AND TEST AGAIN
```

line 34). The new output voltage from the DAC is once more compared with V_u, and the CPU samples the output from the comparator once more.

You will note that the program which increments the data applied to the DAC is similar to the program for the 'ramp-up' sawtooth wave in Listing 8.2. Eventually, a point is reached when V_0 is either equal to or greater than V_u. When this happens, the comparator output falls to logic '0'. This indicates to the CPU that the end-of-conversion (EOC) has been reached, and the result is stored in the location 'RESULT'; alternatively, the result can be displayed on the monitor screen (see Section 10.4).

Since the value of the unknown voltage V_u may change, program control must be restored to the beginning of the sequence, i.e., the binary test value must be restored to zero once more. This process is repeated continuously, enabling the ADC to 'follow' or 'track' changes in V_u.

The program in Listing 8.4 is designed with the 'learning' process in mind, and the time delay routine is included to allow you to investigate the way in which the test data is applied to the DAC part of the ADC. The ADC will run at its top speed if you remove the CALL DELAY instruction in line 31.

Many commercial ADCs use an alternative conversion method known as *successive approximation*, which employs a technique which gives faster conversion than the continuous-balance method, but is not so straightforward. In fact, a commercial unit includes its own software and clock, and merely 'tells' the CPU by means of an interrupt signal (see Chapter 9 for details) that the conversion is complete. The reader is referred to specialist books on the subject for further details (see References for further study).

9
Interrupts

9.1 What is an interrupt?

In real life, you can be carrying out a normal routine function at home or at work when something happens to interrupt you. Interrupts lie in one of two categories, namely either non-maskable or maskable interrupts. A *non-maskable interrupt* (NMI) is one you cannot ignore, such as a burst water pipe, and must be attended to straight away. A *maskable interrupt* is one which can be masked out or ignored; for example, if the telephone rings you can choose either to ignore it, i.e., to mask it out, or you can accept it.

In much the same way, the CPU handles both maskable and non-maskable interrupts. A non-maskable interrupt is reserved for very high-priority events, such as a power supply failure. If such an event occurs, the data in certain registers in the CPU and in some locations in RAM which store vital information can be transferred to a RAM with a battery back-up during the short period of time before the supply voltage falls to a level where the CPU stops working.

Maskable interrupts are used for run-of-the-mill events, such as the keyboard telling the CPU it has some data for it, or for a printer asking for more data.

In the 8086 and 8088 CPUs, interrupts are further subdivided into internal interrupts and external interrupts. An *internal interrupt* is one produced internally by the system, such as a 'division by zero' error or an 'interrupt on overflow'. An *external interrupt* is a signal applied to the CPU by a piece of hardware connected to the CPU, e.g., the keyboard of the computer. The priority given to these interrupts is as follows:

Internal interrupts	highest priority
Non-maskable interrupts (NMI)	
Maskable interrupts	
Single-step interrupt	lowest priority

Strictly speaking, the single-step interrupt is an internal interrupt, but has been given the lowest priority by the manufacturers of the CPU. When several interrupts arrive simultaneously at the CPU, the highest priority interrupt is processed first.

9.2 CPU action when an NMI occurs

The sequence of events which occurs when an NMI occurs is illustrated in Fig. 9.1, and is described below.

1. The flags are pushed onto the stack.
2. The INTR inputs (maskable interrupts) are disabled, and the TF is cleared.
3. The content of the current CS register is pushed onto the stack.
4. The 'next' IP register content is pushed onto the stack.
5. The IP register is loaded with the 16-bit data at the physical address 00008H.
6. The CS register is loaded with the 16-bit data at the physical address 0000AH.

The reason for each of these steps is now described. To ensure an orderly return to the main program, the flags are saved on the stack (Fig. 9.1(a)); when the return to the main program is made after the interrupt, the flags are restored, so ensuring that the operating conditions in the main program are unchanged.

Next, the CPU clears the IF and TF (see Fig. 9.1(b)). The first of these actions disables the INTR inputs, i.e., it disables the maskable interrupts, so that the NMI cannot be interrupted by a maskable interrupt. It also clears the TF, so that single-stepping of the program can no longer occur.

In steps (3) and (4) – see Fig. 9.1(a) – the current CS register and the address of the next instruction which is due to be executed are pushed onto the stack. This ensures that the CPU will be able to determine the correct return address when the interrupt is completed.

At this stage, the CPU has saved the minimum number of registers for a return to the calling program, and has prevented the possibility of the NMI from itself being interrupted. It must now determine where the next instruction is to come from.

It does so by getting data from the *interrupt vector table* in the RAM (see Fig. 9.1(c)). This table is discussed in detail in Section 9.3, and it is sufficient here to say that when an NMI occurs, the CPU loads the CS register with the 16-bit data beginning at address 0000AH, and the IP register with the 16-bit data beginning at address 00008H. These values are used in the usual way to calculate the 20-bit starting address of the interrupt routine. The CPU transfers program control to that address, and the interrupt routine is executed.

9.3 The interrupt vector table

The interrupt vector table is a table at the bottom of the RAM area of the memory (see Figs. 9.1(c) and 9.2), in which the addresses to be used for various

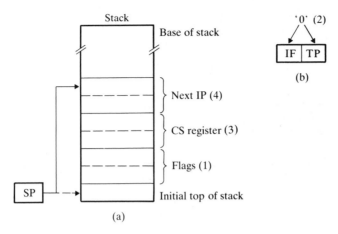

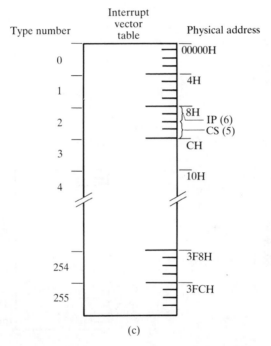

Figure 9.1 The CPU activity when an NMI occurs.

interrupt types are stored. There are 255 *interrupt type numbers*, some being dedicated to specific functions, others being reserved by the manufacture of the CPU for certain functions, and the remaining ones being available for general use.

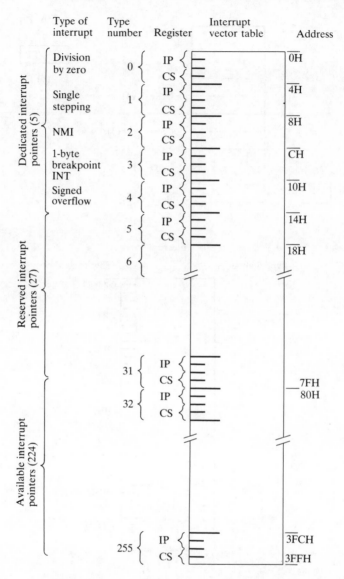

Figure 9.2 The interrupt service address table.

Figure 9.2 shows how these are organized in the RAM of the computer. Each interrupt type has four bytes allocated to it in the table; two bytes contain a 16-bit value which is available to be transferred to the CS register, and two bytes contain a 16-bit value which is to be transferred to the IP register. The CPU uses these values to determine the address of the starting point of the interrupt routine associated with that type number of interrupt.

The NMI interrupt is designated as a type 2 interrupt, and when an NMI occurs, the CPU fills the CS register with the 16-bit value commencing at address 0AH and fills the IP register with the 16-bit value commencing at address 8H. The starting address in the interrupt table for a given type number is calculated as follows:

address in interrupt table $= 4 \times$ interrupt type number

For the interrupt type number 255 this is

address in interrupt table $= 4 \times 255 = 1020 = 3FCH$

The first five interrupt type numbers (types 0–4, inclusive) are dedicated to specific purposes as follows. Whenever the program calls for any number to be divided by zero, the CPU generates an 'internal' type 0 interrupt (try doing this with the division program in Chapter 4 and see what happens!). The type 1 interrupt is used whenever you use the single-stepping mode in DEBUG. The type 2 interrupt is dedicated to the NMI, and was discussed earlier. The type 3 interrupt is dedicated to the breakpoint interrupt; the INT 3 interrupt generates a 1-byte instruction, and is easily planted at any point in a program. It enables you to 'break' into a program and revert, say, to the single-stepping mode at a selected instruction. The type 4 interrupt can be produced by a signed overflow, but is not automatically generated by the CPU when a signed overflow occurs, and must be invoked by the programmer. The instruction set of the 8086 and 8088 does, however, provide an INTO instruction (INTerrupt on Overflow) which produces a type 4 interrupt, and should follow every signed arithmetic instruction whenever there is the possibility of an overflow.

The system designer has 224 interrupt types available (types 32–255, inclusive), which can be used for the peripherals of his system such as disks, printers, etc.

9.4 CPU action when a maskable interrupt occurs

Before the CPU will acknowledge any maskable interrupt, the interrupt flag must be set by means of an STI instruction (SeT Interrupt flag); this instruction must be executed *before* the program incorporating the interrupt is started and *after* the starting address of the interrupt routine has been entered in the interrupt vector table. For the moment we will assume that the starting address of the interrupt routine address has been inserted in the interrupt vector table; a method of entering the interrupt routine address in the table is discussed in Section 9.7.

The steps taken when the CPU receives an interrupt signal on its maskable interrupt pin (INTR – see also Chapter 2) are as follows:

1. The CPU acknowledges receipt of the interrupt signal by driving its interrupt acknowledge pin low ($\overline{\text{INTA}}$ – see Chapter 2).

2. On receiving the interrupt acknowledge signal, the interrupt controller chip puts the interrupt type number on the data bus (this is a number in the range 0–255), and the CPU reads it.
3. The CPU pushes the flags onto the stack.
4. The maskable interrupts and the single-step mode are disabled.
5. The content of the CS register and the 'next' IP content are pushed onto the stack.
6. The IP register is loaded with data from the memory address at (type no. × 4) and (type no. × 4) + 1 [these are in the interrupt table], where type no. = type number of the interrupt.
7. The CS register is loaded with two bytes of data from the memory address at (type no. × 4) + 2 and (type no. × 4) + 3 [these are also in the interrupt table].
8. The CPU calculates the 20-bit address of the first instruction on the interrupt routine from the values obtained in steps 6 and 7, and executes the instruction at that address.

The conditions in the stack and the relevant registers at the end of this sequence are illustrated in Fig. 9.3.

Other than steps 1 and 2, which are used to determine the interrupt type number, the processes involved are generally similar to those for the NMI (see also Figs. 9.1 and 9.2). Steps 3–8, inclusive, are identical to the way in which the NMI is processed with the exception that the addresses calculated in steps 6 and 7 above depend on the interrupt type number. In this chapter we will assume that our interrupt has type number 255.

9.5   Returning from an interrupt

The general operation of an interrupt routine is similar to that for a subroutine or procedure with the exception that, since the content of the flags register and

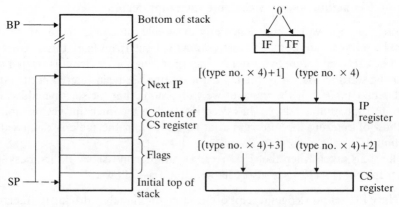

Figure 9.3   Conditions when a maskable interrupt occurs.

the CS register were pushed onto the stack when the interrupt occurred, they must be restored when a return is made from the interrupt. This is accomplished by terminating the interrupt routine by an IRET instruction (Interrupt RETurn).

9.6   The 8259 interrupt controller

The 8086 and 8088 are sophisticated devices, and are capable of supporting many peripherals, each of which may demand the use of the CPU at any time. As you have seen already, the CPU can handle up to 255 interrupts, and the 8259 interrupt controller chip has been designed to 'manage' or control eight of these interrupting devices. It is possible to cascade 8259 chips, so that one 'master' interrupt controller can handle $8 \times 8 = 64$ interrupting sources.

It is the interrupt controller which receives the initial interrupt request from the peripherals; the interrupt controller sends the interrupt request signal to the CPU and, when the interrupt request has been acknowledged, it puts the interrupt type number on the data bus.

The seven interrupting sources connected to the 8259 chip can be connected to any one of its pins marked from source 0 to source 7. The chip provides an order of priority, with source 0 having the highest priority and source 7 the lowest priority. When several interrupts occur simultaneously, the 8259 deals with the highest-priority interrupt first.

The chip has an *interrupt mask register (IMR)*, and it is the programmer's responsibility to 'unmask' any interrupts required by the program and to 'mask out' any interrupts which are not needed.

An interrupt is unmasked or is 'allowed' if the appropriate bit in the IMR is '0', and is masked out if the bit is '1'. Thus, if the IMR contains 01111101B, then interrupt requests corresponding to bits 1 and 7 are unmasked, i.e., they are 'allowed', and all other interrupts are masked out. It is assumed in the text that our 8259 chip handles interrupt numbers 248–255, inclusive, and that the interrupt type number 255 (or interrupt) is connected to bit 7 of the IMR. If we wish to enable only interrupt type number 255 and to disable types 248–254, inclusive, the hex value 7F must be loaded into the IMR. The address of the IMR depends on the way that the I/O mapped addresses have been arranged; in our case, the address of the IMR is 2H.

Having correctly set up the interrupt mask, it is important to remember that you must also *set the interrupt flag* in the CPU before any maskable interrupts can be handled. Failure to do so means that none of the maskable interrupts will be acknowledged.

9.7   An interrupt program

In the following we will consider a program (see Listing 9.1) which handles data from switches connected to port B of an 8255 PPI and sends the signals to LEDs

```
 1: ;****INTERRUPT PROGRAM – LISTING 9.1****
 2: ;****STACK SEGMENT****
 3: MY_STACK    SEGMENT PARA                        STACK
 4:             DB      100H    DUP(?)
 5: MY_STACK    ENDS
 6: ;****CODE SEGMENT****
 7: MY_CODE SEGMENT
 8:         ASSUME SS:MY_STACK,CS:MY_CODE
 9: PORTA    EQU    40H              ;PROGRAM ADDRESSES AND DATA
10: PORTB    EQU    42H
11: PORTC    EQU    44H
12: CONREG   EQU    46H
13: CONBYTE  EQU    8BH
14: IMR      EQU    2H               ;INTERRUPT MASK REGISTER ADDRESS
15: IMRBYTE  EQU    7FH              ;BYTE USED TO MASK IMR
16: VECT_TAB EQU    0H               ;INTERRUPT VECTOR TABLE ADDRESS
17: INT_TYPE EQU    3FCH             ;INTERRUPT TYPE NUMBER × 4 (HEX)
18: START:   MOV    AL,CONBYTE       ;INITIALIZE 8255 PPI
19:          OUT    CONREG,AL
20:          MOV    AX,VECT_TAB      ;(DS) = START OF VECTOR TABLE
21:          MOV    DS,AX
22:          MOV    BX,INT_TYPE      ;MOV OFFSET OF INT_TYPE INTO BX
23:          LEA    AX,INT_ROUTINE   ;LOAD INT ROUTINE ADDRESS INTO
24:                                  ;INTERRUPT VECTOR TABLE
25:          MOV    [BX],AX
26:          MOV    AX,CS            ;LOAD (CS) INTO VECTOR TABLE
27:          MOV    [BX+2],AX
28:          MOV    AL,IMRBYTE       ;ENABLE INTERRUPT TYPE 255
29:          OUT    IMR,AL           ;AND DISABLE TYPES 248–254
30:          STI                     ;ENABLE MASKABLE INTERRUPTS
31: ;****MAIN PROGRAM****
32: GET:     IN     AL,PORTB         ;READ SWITCHES
33:          AND    AL,7FH           ;MASK OUT M.S.B.
34:          OUT    PORTA,AL         ;AND DISPLAY ON LEDs
```

```
35:                         JMP     GET
36: ;****INTERRUPT ROUTINE****
37: INT_ROUTINE:    PUSH    AX          ;SAVE THE CONTENTS OF AX
38:                 MOV     AL,80H      ;TURN ON MOST SIGNIFICANT LED
39:                 OUT     PORTA,AL
40:                 CALL    DELAY
41: STAY:           IN      AL,PORTB    ;READ SWITCHES
42:                 AND     AL,80H      ;TEST BIT 7
43:                 JNZ     STAY        ;REMAIN IN INTERRUPT SERVICE
44:                                     ;ROUTINE IF BIT 7 = 1
45:                 POP     AX          ;RESTORE CONTENTS OF REGISTER AX
46:                 IRET                ;RETURN FROM INTERRUPT
47: ;****DELAY PROCEDURE****
48: DELAY           PROC
49:                 MOV     CX,10H
50: LONG:           MOV     DX,2000H
51: TEST:           DEC     DX
52:                 JNZ     TEST
53:                 LOOP    LONG
54:                 RET
55: DELAY           ENDP
56: MY_CODE ENDS
57:                 END     START
```

connected to port A of the same chip (see Chapter 7 for details of the I/O module).

Lines 1–13 of the program, inclusive, set up the stack segment and the data for the 8255 PPI which controls the I/O module. Line 14 sets up the address of the IMR of the interrupt controller, and line 15 establishes the byte of data (7FH) which is to be used as an interrupt mask (see Section 9.6 for details). Line 16 gives the base address of the interrupt vector table, and line 17 gives the offset of the first byte of data in the interrupt table of interrupt type 255 (see also Fig. 9.2). As with earlier I/O programs, lines 18 and 19 initialize the 8255 PPI so that port A acts as an output port, and ports B and C act as input ports.

Lines 20–30, inclusive, are needed to initialize the interrupt system as follows. Lines 20 and 21 move the base address of the vector table into the data segment register (Fig. 9.4 illustrates these steps graphically), and line 22 moves the offset of the interrupt type number, i.e., 3FCH, into register BX. Next, the instructions in lines 23 and 25 move the effective address of interrupt routine type 255 into the two bytes in the interrupt vector table commencing at the address given by the contents of register BX, i.e., address 03FCH. Lines 26 and 27 move the 16-bit code segment base address into the next two bytes in the interrupt vector table (since the code segment of the interrupt routine is the same as that of the main program, the current CS contents are moved into the vector table).

At this point the contents of important addresses in the vector table are as shown in Fig. 9.5. Next, the instructions in lines 28 and 29 unmask interrupt type 255 and mask out interrupt types 248–254, inclusive. Finally, line 30 enables all the unmasked interrupts in the system.

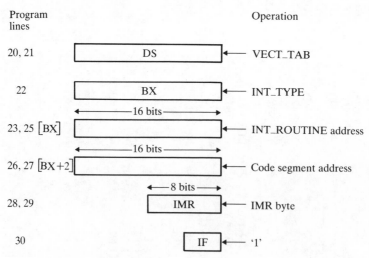

Figure 9.4 Pictorial representation of initializing interrupt type 255.

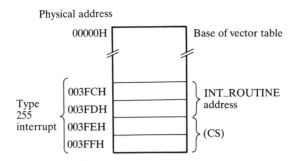

Figure 9.5 The contents of some locations in the interrupt vector table.

The main program in lines 32–35, inclusive, simply read the state of the seven switches connected to lines PB0–PB6, inclusive, of port B, and outputs the data to the seven LEDs connected to lines PA0–PA6, respectively.

An interrupt occurs when a logic '1' is applied (from, say, a push-button switch on the peripheral) to the appropriate line of the interrupt controller. This signal is passed to the INTR line of the CPU, and the CPU goes through the steps outlined in Section 9.4. At this stage you are reminded that not only is the IF cleared (preventing the interrupt routine from itself being interrupted by any other maskable interrupt), but that the flags are pushed onto the stack.

Also at this time, the CPU has loaded the IP register with the INT_ROUTINE offset from the vector table addresses 3FCH and 3FDH, and has loaded the CS register with the address of the 'new' code segment (which is also the original code segment in our case) from locations 3FEH and 3FFH in the vector table. At this stage the CPU calculates the address of the first instruction in the interrupt routine, and then it executes it.

The interrupt routine in lines 37–46, inclusive, does the following. If line PB7 of the 8255 PPI has a '0' on it, the LED connected to PA7 is illuminated and all other LEDs are extinguished, this condition is held on for the period of time set by the delay procedure in lines 48–55, inclusive. However, if line PB7 has a '1' applied to it, the CPU is retained in the interrupt routine and the LED connected to the most significant bit of port A of the 8255 PPI remains illuminated until the logic level on line PB7 falls to '0'. When the latter condition applies, a return is made to the main program.

The IRET instruction in line 46 ensures that the flags are POPped from the stack and into the flag register. This means that once the interrupt flag has been set in line 30, it is not necessary to reset the interrupt flag at the end of the interrupt routine; that is, the IRET instruction resets the IF and, in this way, the interrupt routine is made re-entrant.

10
Text operations and decimal multiplication

10.1 Introduction to string manipulation instructions

A string is a set of characters which are stored in the memory of a computer. The 8086 and 8088 have a number of very powerful instructions which allow you to manipulate strings, and include

MOVe a String   (MOVS)
CoMPare Strings   (CMPS)
SCAn a String   (SCAS)
LOaD a String   (LODS)
STOre a String   (STOS)

Each of the above instructions can handle a byte or a word and, by appending the letter B or W to the instruction, the computer is aware whether a byte or a word is being handled. That is, **MOVSB** moves a byte and **MOVSW** moves a word.

When handling strings, the source string is addressed by the SI (Source Index) register, and the destination string is addressed by the DI (Destination Index) register; these registers must be loaded into the program with the effective address of the source and destination strings, respectively.

The source string is assumed to exist in the data segment, and the destination string is assumed to exist in the extra segment. Provided that the program is not too large, the DS and ES registers can be set to the same value so that the two segments completely overlap.

To summarize, the *source string* resides in the *data segment*, and the effective address of the source string is contained in the *SI register*. The *destination string* resides in the *extra segment*, and the effective address of the destination string is contained in the *DI register*. The data segment and the extra segment may completely overlap one another.

142

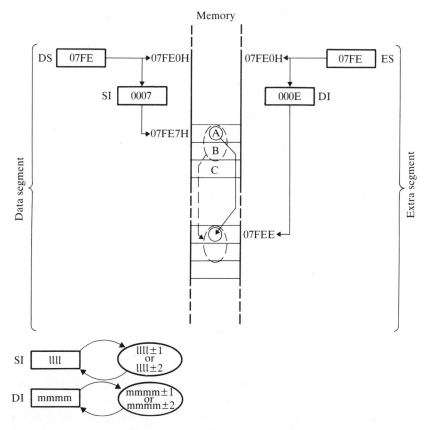

Figure 10.1   The MOVS instruction.

10.2   MOVing Strings (MOVS) and the direction flag (DF)

The execution of a MOVS instruction results in a byte or a word being moved
from the source to its destination. Suppose that the DS and ES registers both
contain 07FEH, as shown in Fig. 10.1, so that the data segment and the extra
segment completely overlap one another. We will also assume that the SI
register contains the displacement 07H and the DI register contains 0EH.

The 'direction' in which the string is to be moved is controlled by the
condition of the *direction flag* (DF). If DF is cleared (DF = 0), then the SI and
DI registers are auto-incremented during each instruction involving a string.
This means that after the first MOVS instruction involving the movement of a
byte, the SI and DI registers contain 08 and 0FH, respectively; after the second
MOVS instruction they contain 09 and 10H, respectively, and so on. However,
if the DF flag is set (DF = 1), the SI and DI registers are auto-decremented
during each string instruction. This enables the CPU to move along a string in

either a forward or reverse direction in either byte-by-byte or word-by-word fashion.

If the string stored in the memory is 'ABCDEFG', and the DF is cleared, the operation of the first MOVS instruction causes the string character addressed by the SI register in the data segment to be moved to the location addressed by the DI register in the extra segment. If the instruction involves a byte, then the ASCII character 'A' (stored as 41H) is moved in the manner shown in Fig. 10.1; at the same time, the SI and DI registers are auto-incremented. If the instruction involves a word, then the two characteris 'AB' are moved (shown in broken line in Fig. 10.1); in this case, the SI and DI registers are incremented by two.

That is, after the MOVS byte instruction, the SI register addresses the location containing the character 'B' (stored as 42H), and the DI register addresses the next memory location above 07FEFH. The CPU is now ready to move the character 'B' to the new address indicated by the DI register in the extra segment.

In order to handle complete strings, the CPU must be able to repeat the MOVS instruction until all the characters in the nominated string have been moved. This is done by the REP instruction (REPeat). The REP instruction is used as a prefix to the MOVS instruction (and also with other string instructions – see later), and its mnemonic is in the form

REP MOVS destination,source

and means 'REPeat MOVing the String from the source to the destination until the end of the string is reached'. Alternative mnemonics for the REP instruction are REPE (REPeat while Equal) and REPZ (REPeat while Zero). Other REPeat instructions are REPNE (REPeat while Not Equal) and REPNZ (REPeat while Not Zero), both having the same effect as one another.

The number of characters to be handled by the REP instruction (i.e., the 'length' of the string) is given by the value in the CX register; this value is auto-decremented each time the REP instruction is encountered. Suppose that a program contains the following instructions:

STRING_LEN   EQU   7

MOV   CX   STRING_LEN
.
.
.

REP   MOVS   SPACE_2,STRING

The program will move (transfer a copy of) a string (which is also called STRING) of length 7 characters in the data segment to a string call SPACE_2 in the extra segment. A program which does this by *moving the string forward in the memory* is contained in Listing 10.1.

```
 1: ;****MOVING TEXT FORWARD IN MEMORY – LISTING 10.1****
 2: ;****STACK SEGMENT****
 3: MY_STACK        SEGMENT  PARA       STACK
 4:              DB    100H    DUP(0H)
 5: MY_STACK        ENDS
 6: ;****DATA SEGMENT****
 7: MY_DATA SEGMENT
 8: SPACE_1     DB    7          DUP(0H)
 9: STRING      DB    'ABCDEFG'
10: SPACE_2     DB    7          DUP(0H)
11: MY_DATA ENDS
12: ;****CODE SEGMENT****
13: MY_CODE SEGMENT
14:         ASSUME SS:MY_STACK,DS:MY_DATA,ES:MY_DATA,CS:MY_CODE
15: STRING_LEN       EQU      7
16:                                    ;FOR USE LATER
17: START:  MOV   AX,MY_DATA
18:         MOV   DS,AX            ;ESTABLISH DATA SEGMENT
19:         MOV   ES,AX            ;ESTABLISH EXTRA SEGMENT
20:         MOV   CX,STRING_LEN    ;SET UP STRING LENGTH COUNTER
21:         LEA   SI,STRING        ;LOAD ADDRESS OF STRING
22:         LEA   DI,SPACE_2       ;LOAD ADDRESS OF NEW STRING
23:         CLD                    ;FORWARD MOVE
24:                                ;FOR USE LATER
25:         REP   MOVS SPACE_2,STRING   ;MOVE STRING
26:         INT   23H              ;END OF PROGRAM
27: MY_CODE ENDS
28: END     START
```

Lines 8–10 of the program allocate 21 bytes of memory for string handling; the first and last seven bytes contain 'spaces', and the centre seven contain the STRING 'ABCDEFG'. Lines 18 and 19 ensure that the data segment and extra segment completely overlap. The string length is established in register CX by lines 15 and 20, and lines 21 and 22 load the effective address of the source string (STRING) and the destination of the data (SPACE_2) in the SI and DI registers, respectively. The CLD instruction in line 23 CLears the Direction flag, so that the SI and DI registers will auto-increment when the MOVS instruction is encountered.

The main program consists of the instruction in line 25. Since STRING and SPACE_2 are defined as byte stores, this instruction causes the STRING to be moved byte-by-byte to the area of memory commencing at address SPACE_2 in the extra segment. Before the REP MOVS instruction is executed, the information in the data and extra segments is as follows (the locations 'pointed to' by the SI and DI registers, together with SPACE_1, STRING and SPACE_2, is as shown below):

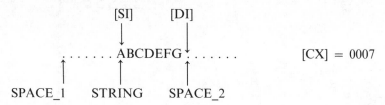

[SI]   [DI]

. . . . . . ABCDEFG . . . . . .   [CX] = 0007

SPACE_1   STRING   SPACE_2

After the instruction in line 25 has been executed the STRING has been moved, and the data and extra segments contain the following:

[SI]   [DI]

. . . . . . ABCDEFGABCDEFG   [CX] = 0000

SPACE_1   STRING   SPACE_2

At this point the SI register has been incremented from 7H to EH, and the DI register has been incremented by 7 to 15H, i.e., it points to the 'next' item (if any) to be moved.

Alternatively, the *string may be moved backwards in the memory* using the program in Listing 10.2. The program is implemented by making the changes

```
 1: ;****MOVING TEXT BACKWARDS IN MEMORY – LISTING 10.2****
21: LEA   SI,STRING+STRING_LEN–1     ;ADDRESS OF TOP OF STRING
22: LEA   DI,SPACE_1+STRING_LEN–1    ;ADDRESS OF TOP OF SPACE_1
23: STD                              ;REVERSE MOVE
24:                                  ;MOVE STRING BACKWARDS
25: REP   MOVS SPACE_1+STRING_LEN–1,STRING+STRING_LEN–1
```

shown to lines 1 and 21–25, inclusive, of Listing 10.1. Line 21 sets up the SI register to point at the *final character* in the source STRING, and line 22 causes the DI register to point to the position in memory where this character is to go (which is the location below where 'A' is stored in the STRING). Just before the REP MOVS instruction is executed, the data stored is as follows:

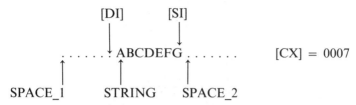

The STD instruction in line 23 causes the SI and DI registers to auto-decrement each time the MOVS instruction is encountered. After the REP MOVS instruction in line 25 has been executed seven times (which is the value in CX), the data segment and the extra segment contain the following:

```
        [DI]        [SI]
         |           |
         ↓           ↓
         ADCDEFGABCDEFG . . . . . .      [CX] = 0000
         ↑           ↑        ↑
   SPACE_1       STRING   SPACE_2
```

10.3   Moving overlapping text in the memory

When using the 8086 or 8088 in a word processor (the line editor EDLIN used for editing assembly language programs is a simple word processor), instructions are available which allow the user to move and modify text. The text you need to move quite frequently overlaps other text in the memory; a number of powerful instructions are available which allow you to deal with this situation.

We will deal here only with the introductory concepts of moving overlapping text, and you can use these to develop an outline of a simple text editor.

The program is contained in Listing 10.3, and is a modification of Listing 10.1 (only the modified lines are shown in Listing 10.3). We consider the case where the text is to be moved 'forward' four places with respect to the old position of the string – see Fig. 10.2. If we set the SI and DI registers to the 'start' of the respective strings, and move the text in a 'forward' direction, then, if the data and extra segments completely overlap (as they do here), the 'first' character in the string which is moved overwrites the fifth character in the 'old' string.

Clearly, if we need to move a string forward to an overlapping position, the SI and DI registers must initially point to the 'top' of the respective strings, and the computer must do a 'backward' string movement. In this case, the computer

```
 1: ;****MOVING OVERLAPPING TEXT IN MEMORY – LISTING 10.3****
16:    STRING_2 EQU STRING+4            ;STARTING POSITION OF NEW STRING
17: START:  MOV  AX,MY_DATA
18:         MOV  DS,AX                   ;ESTABLISH DATA SEGMENT
19:         MOV  ES,AX                   ;ESTABLISH EXTRA SEGMENT
20:         MOV  CX,STRING_LEN           ;SET UP STRING LENGTH COUNTER
21:         LEA  SI,STRING+STRING_LEN–1  ;ADDRESS OF TOP OF STRING
22:         LEA  DI,STRING_2+STRING_LEN–1 ;ADDRESS OF TOP OF STRING_2
23:         STD                          ;REVERSE MOVE
24:                                      ;MOVE STRING BACKWARDS
25:         REP  MOVS STRING_2+STRING_LEN–1,STRING+STRING_LEN–1
```

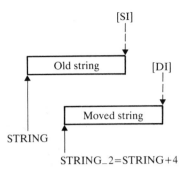

Figure 10.2 Moving overlapping text in the memory.

does not overwrite any of the characters in the old string which remain uncopied. That is, the SI and DI registers must point to the positions shown in broken line in Fig. 10.2.

Turning now to Listing 10.3, line 16 sets up STRING_2 to the address of the first character in the 'moved' string – refer to Fig. 10.2. Lines 21 and 22 establish the address of the top of the old STRING and the top of the 'moved' string in SI and DI, respectively. The SI and DI registers are set to the auto-decrement mode by the STD instruction in line 23, and the string is moved 'backward' by line 25. Before line 25 is executed, the condition of the data segment and the extra segment are as follows:

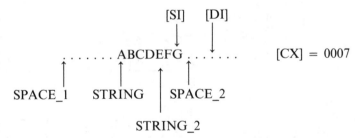

After the REP MOVS instruction has been executed once, the memory condition is as follows:

```
1:  ;****MESSAGE HANDLING – LISTING 10.4****
2:  ;****STACK SEGMENT****
3:  MY_STACK      SEGMENT   PARA      STACK
4:                DB        100H      DUP(?)
5:  MY_STACK      ENDS
6:  ;****DATA SEGMENT****
7:  MY_DATA       SEGMENT
8:  ;
9:  ;****MESSAGES****
10: ;
11: MSG_A         DB        'THIS IS A MESSAGE . . .'
12: MSG_B         DB        'THAT WAS A PROGRAM . .'
13: MSG_C         DB        'GET SOME DISKS . . . . . .'
14: MY_DATA ENDS
15: ;****CODE SEGMENT****
16: MY_CODE SEGMENT
17:         ASSUME SS:MY_STACK,DS:MY_DATA,CS:MY_CODE
18: START:        MOV   AX,MY_DATA     ;SET UP DATA SEGMENT ADDRESSABILITY
19:               MOV   DS,AX
20:               MOV   DL,3           ;SET UP MESSAGE COUNTER
21:               LEA   BX,MSG_A       ;POINT TO START OF MESSAGES
22: NEXT:         CALL  GET_MSG        ;GET MESSAGE
23:               DEC   DL             ;DECREMENT MESSAGE COUNTER
24:               JZ    FINISH         ;FINISH IF ALL MESSAGES PRINTED
25:               JMP   NEXT           ;GET NEXT MESSAGE
26: FINISH:       INT   23H            ;END OF PROGRAM
27: ;
28: ;****GET MESSAGE****
29: ;
30: GET_MSG       PROC
31:               MOV   CX,20          ;GET MESSAGE LENGTH
32: DISPLAY:      MOV   AL,[BX]        ;GET NEXT CHARACTER IN MESSAGE
33:               CALL  PRINT_CHAR     ;AND PRINT IT
34:               INC   BX             ;POINT TO NEXT CHARACTER
```

```
35:              LOOP      DISPLAY              ;REPEAT FOR COMPLETE MESSAGE
36:              MOV       AL,0DH               ;CARRIAGE RETURN
37:              CALL      PRINT_CHAR
38:              MOV       AL,0AH               ;LINE FEED
39:              CALL      PRINT_CHAR
40:              RET                            ;RETURN FOR MORE MESSAGES
41: GET_MSG      ENDP
42: ;
43: ;****CHARACTER PRINTING PROCEDURE****
44: ;
45: PRINT_CHAR   PROC
46:              PUSH      BX                   ;SAVE (BX)
47:              MOV       BX,0                 ;SELECT DISPLAY PAGE 0
48:              MOV       AH,14                ;LOAD CODE FOR ASCII OUTPUT
49:              INT       10H                  ;TRANSFER CONTROL TO BIOS VDU DRIVER
50:              POP       BX                   ;RESTORE (BX)
51:              RET                            ;RETURN FOR NEXT CHARACTER
52: PRINT_CHAR   ENDP
53: MY_CODE ENDS
54: END          START
```

On completion of the REP MOVS instruction, the memory condition is as follows:

10.4 Handling messages on the VDU

In Chapter 3, we mentioned that the BIOS made use of some of the locations in the interrupt vector table in order to handle some of the peripherals such as the diskette, the serial I/O, the keyboard and the printer. Interrupt type 10H (INT 10H) is used to send data to the monitor, and we consider in this section how to use it to send messages to the screen. The operating mode of the video I/O is set by the values stored in registers AH and BX. To print a character on the screen at the current cursor position, the values AH = 14 and BX = 0 must be established. The ASCII code for the character to be sent to the screen must be in the AL register.

A program which sends three strings of text to the screen is contained in Listing 10.4, and is described below. The program displays the three messages in lines 11–13 of the program. The main program resides in lines 18–26, inclusive, and calls on procedures GET_MSG and PRINT_CHAR. Lines 31 to 35, inclusive, of GET_MSG 'reads' each character in each message, and calls on PRINT_CHAR to 'print' it on the screen of the monitor.

Since register BX is used by GET_MSG, the content of BX is saved on the stack (see line 46) when PRINT_CHAR is called. PRINT_CHAR establishes the condition for displaying the character which has been put in AL by GET_MSG; it does so by moving 0 and 14 into BX and AH, respectively (see also the first paragraph of this section). The INT 10H instruction in line 49 causes the character to be printed on the screen.

When each 20-character string has been printed, lines 36–39, inclusive, result in a 'carriage return' and a 'line feed' to occur (see also Appendix B), causing the screen cursor to move to the starting position of the next message. The program continues until all the messages have been printed.

10.5 Loading strings and storing strings

The LODS instruction (LOaD String) is used to load either a byte of data into AL or a word into AX. The STOS instruction (STOre String) is used to store either a byte of data which is in AL, or a word which is in AX.

```
 1: ;****UNPACKED BCD ADDITION – LISTING 10.5****
 2: ;****STACK SEGMENT****
 3: MY_STACK        SEGMENT   PARA      STACK
 4:                 DB        100H      DUP(?)
 5: MY_STACK        ENDS
 6: ;****DATA SEGMENT****
 7: MY_DATA SEGMENT
 8: VAL_1           DB        '5','6','9','8','0'      ;VAL_1 = 08965
 9: VAL_2           DB        '4','8','6','9','0'      VAL_ = 09684
10: MY_DATA ENDS
11: ;****CODE SEGMENT****
12: MY_CODE SEGMENT
13:         ASSUME SS:MY_STACK,DS:MY_DATA,ES:MY_DATA,CS:MY_CODE
14: START:  MOV       AX,MY_DATA
15:         MOV       DS,AX                    ;ESTABLISH DATA SEGMENT
16:         MOV       ES,AX                    ;ESTABLISH EXTRA SEGMENT
17:         CLC                                ;NO INITIAL CARRY
18:         CLD                                ;FORWARD STRINGS
19:         LEA       SI,VAL_1                 ;STRING POINTERS
20:         LEA       DI,VAL_2
21: VAL_LEN EQU       5                        ;'LENGTH' OF VALUES
22:         MOV       CX,VAL_LEN               ;SET UP COUNTER
23: SUM:    LODS      VAL_1                    ;GET ELEMENT FROM VAL_1
24:         ADC       AL,[DI]                  ;ADD WITH CARRY ELEMENT FROM VAL_1
25:         AAA                                ;CORRECT FOR ASCII ADDITION
26:         STOSB                              ;STORE RESULT IN VAL_2
27:         DEC       CX                       ;DECREMENT COUNTER
28:         JNZ       SUM                      ;IF (CX) = 0, ADD NEXT ELEMENTS
29:         INT       23H                      ;ELSE END OF PROGRAM
30: MY_CODE ENDS
31: END             START
```

The byte or word accessed by a LODS instruction is in the data segment, and is addressed by the value in the DI register as shown in Fig. 10.3(a).

The byte (or word) stored in the memory by a STOS instruction is either in AL (byte) or AX (word), and is stored in the extra segment at the effective address given by the value in the DI register.

The way in which the string is accessed depends on the condition of the DF. If DF = 0, the content of the SI register is auto-incremented by each string instruction, and is decremented if DF = 1.

The effect of a LODS instruction (with DF = 0) is shown in Fig. 10.3. The status of the computer before the LODS instruction is shown in diagram (a), and after the instruction has been executed (see diagram (b)), the byte of data in location 07FE3H is moved into AL. At the same time, the SI register is incremented so that it 'points' to the next byte of data.

If the source string is specified in words, then the word commencing at the location addressed by SI is moved into AX.

The effect of a STOS instruction (with DF = 0) is shown in diagrams (c) and (d) of Fig. 10.3. The STOS instruction stores the byte of data in AL (or word of data in AX) at the effective address in the data segment given by the value in the DI register. The DI register is then incremented so that it points to the next available address in the extra segment.

As with the MOVS instruction, the LODS and STOS instructions can be repeated by using the REP instruction in association with them, i.e., REP STOS; the number of REPeats is set by the value in the CX register.

An example of the use of LODS and STOS instructions is given in the unpacked BCD addition program in Listing 10.5. This program *adds the ASCII 'decimal' string VAL_1 to the decimal string VAL_2*, leaving the result in VAL_2. The main program begins in line 23, where it LOaDs an element of string VAL_1 into register AL, and then adds it to the character from the equivalent 'position' in string VAL_2. After making the necessary ASCII adjustment for addition (the AAA instruction in line 25 leaves the unpacked BCD value in AL), the STOSB instruction in line 26 stores the result in the equivalent position in VAL_2. This process is repeated until the two strings have been added together (the 'length' of the strings is stored in CX – see lines 21 and 22). You will note that the most significant digit in VAL_1 and in VAL_2 is zero in both cases; this allows the program to use the same addition routine to account for any 'carry' produced by the addition of the penultimate digits. Since the data segment and the extra segment completely overlap in this program, the following information (commencing with the lowest address in the two segments) is stored in them *before* the addition process.

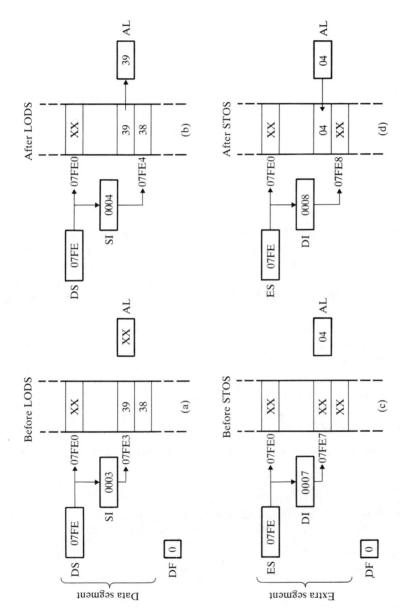

Figure 10.3 Byte movement (a) before LODS, (b) after LODS, (c) before STOS, (d) after STOS.

VAL_1 (ASCII)   VAL_2 (ASCII)

'5'	'6'	'9'	'8'	'0'	'4'	'8'	'6'	'9'	'0'		
35	36	39	38	30	34	38	36	39	30	XX	[CX] = 0005

↑   ↑
[SI]   [DI]

After the addition process, the content of the two segments is

VAL_1 (ASCII)   SUM

'5'	'6'	'9'	'8'	'0'	9	4	6	8	1		
25	36	39	38	30	09	64	06	08	01	XX	[CX] = 0000

                    ↑   ↑
                    [SI]   [DI]

You will note that the SUM of 18649 is stored in unpacked BCD form.

When dealing with arithmetic processes earlier in the book, it was mentioned that decimal multiplication could not be performed using packed BCD numbers. The program in Listing 10.6 illustrates the basis of *decimal multiplication* of the string VAL_1 (= 8965) and VAL_2 (= 5). The reader will find it an interesting exercise to explain the operation of the program.

Since the data segment and the extra segment completely overlay one another, the following data is found in the two segments (commencing at the lowest address) before the multiplication:

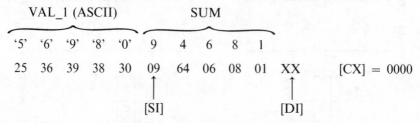

VAL_1 (ASCII)   VAL_2 (ASCII)   RESULT

'5'	'6'	'9'	'8'	'0'	'5'	00	00	00	00	00	XX	[CX] = 0005
35	36	39	38	30	35							

↑   ↑
[SI]   [DI]

On completion of the program, the corresponding values are as listed below. Once again, the RESULT (= 44825) is in unpacked BCD form.

VAL_1 (ASCII)   VAL_2   RESULT

'5'	'6'	'9'	'8'	'0'	5	5	2	8	4	4		
35	36	39	38	30	05	05	02	08	04	04	XX	[CX] = 0000

                    ↑   ↑
                    [SI]   [DI]

```
 1:  ;****UNPACKED BCD MULTIPLICATION – LISTING 10.6****
 2:  ;****STACK SEGMENT****
 3:  MY_STACK        DB              SEGMENT    PARA    STACK
 4:                                  100H       DUP(?)
 5:  MY_STACK        ENDS
 6:  ;****DATA SEGMENT****
 7:  MY_DATA SEGMENT
 8:  VAL_1           DB      '5','6','9','8','0'     ;VAL_1 = 08965
 9:  VAL_2           DB      '5'                     ;VAL_2 = 5
10:  RESULT          DB      5          DUP(0)       ;SPACE FOR RESULT
11:  MY_DATA ENDS
12:  ;****CODE SEGMENT****
13:  MY_CODE SEGMENT
14:          ASSUME SS:MY_STACK,DS:MY_DATA,ES:MY_DATA,CS:MY_CODE
15:  START:  MOV     AX,MY_DATA
16:          MOV     DS,AX                   ;ESTABLISH DATA SEGMENT
17:          MOV     ES,AX                   ;ESTABLISH EXTRA SEGMENT
18:          CLD                             ;FORWARD STRINGS
19:          LEA     SI,VAL_1                ;STRING POINTERS
20:          LEA     DI,RESULT
21:  VAL_LEN EQU     5                       ;'LENGTH' OF VAL_1 AND RESULT
22:          MOV     CX,VAL_LEN              ;SET UP COUNTER
23:          AND     VAL_2,0FH               ;CLEAR HIGH-ORDER BITS OF VAL_2
24:  MULTIPLY: LODS  VAL_1                   ;GET ELEMENT FROM VAL_1
25:          AND     AL,0FH                  ;CLEAR HIGH-ORDER BITS OF ELEMENT
26:          MUL     VAL_2                   ;MULTIPLY BY VAL_2
27:          AAM                             ;ASCII ADJUST FOR MULTIPLICATION
28:          ADD     AL,[DI]                 ;ADD CARRY
29:          AAA                             ;ASCII ADJUST FOR ADDITION
30:          STOSB                           ;STORE ANSWER IN 'RESULT'
31:          MOV     [DI],AH                 ;MOVE CARRY INTO [DI]
32:          DEC     CX                      ;DECREMENT COUNTER
33:          JNZ     MULTIPLY                ;IF (CX) NOT 0, CONTINUE MULTIPLYING
34:          INT     23H                     ;ELSE END PROGRAM
35:  MY_CODE ENDS
36:  END     START
```

10.6 Scanning a string for a character

The SCAS instruction (SCAn a String for a character) enables the CPU to scan a string in its extra segment for a specific character. The mnemonic is

SCAS destination_string

e.g., SCAS STRING, where STRING is in the extra segment. The destination string may be in either byte or word form and, if DF = 0, it is scanned in the forward direction or, if DF = 1, it is scanned in the reverse direction.

The SCAS instruction subtracts the destination string element (byte or word) addressed by the DI register either from the content of AL (if the specified character is a byte) or from AX (if it is a word). The instruction does not alter the value in the destination string or in the A-register, but it updates the flags to indicate the result; it also updates the DI register to point at the next string element.

The SCAS instruction may also be used to scan a complete string by using it with one of the repeat prefixes, e.g., REPE, REPZ, REPNE or REPNZ. An example of the string-scan instruction REPNE SCAS is illustrated in Listing 10.7, which is a modification of Listing 10.1, in which the modified lines are shown.

```
 1:  ;****USE OF THE SCAS INSTRUCTION – LISTING 10.7****
21:      ;
22:      LEA      DI,STRING       ;LOAD ADDRESS OF STRING
23:      CLD                      ;FORWARD MOVE
24:      MOV      AL,'E'          ;CHARACTER TO BE FOUND
25:      REPNE    SCAS STRING     ;SCAN STRING
```

The REPNE prefix allows the string to be scanned (the length of the string being stored in register CX) whilst the character being scanned is not equal to the sample data in AL (byte) or AX (word). The string is specified in byte form in Listing 10.7, so that the STRING character is compared with the byte in AL. This byte (which is the character 'E' or 45H) is moved into AL in line 24.

The mechanics of operation of the instruction are shown in Fig. 10.4. Initially, the DI register addresses the letter 'A' (= 41H) in the memory location 07FE7H in the extra segment. When 'E' is subtracted from this value, the result is non-zero and the zero flag is cleared; the SCAS instruction also increments the DI register when the instruction is executed, so that it points to the location containing the letter 'B'. Additionally, the REPNE instruction causes the CPU to decrement the CX register.

The REPNE instruction also causes the CPU to look at the ZF and, since this is cleared, the composite instruction REPNE SCAS moves on to see if the next character is the letter 'E'.

Finally, when DI = 000BH (and when CX = 0003H), the CPU finds that the character in AL ('E') is equal to the character in the STRING.; at this stage

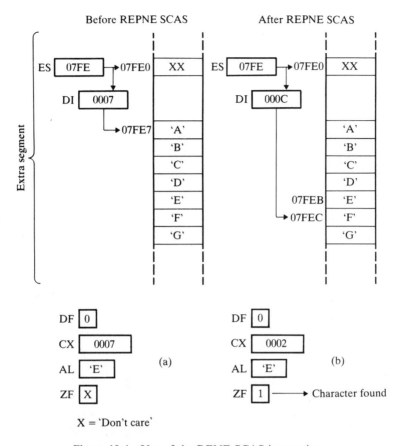

X = 'Don't care'

Figure 10.4 Use of the RENE SCAS instruction.

the composite instruction increments DI to 000CH and increments CX to 0002. Having discovered equality between the two characters, the computer then leaves the REPNE SCAS instruction and executes the next instruction in sequence (which, in our case, terminates the program). The situation in the pointer registers is as shown in Fig. 10.4(b).

10.7 Comparing strings

The CMPS instruction (CoMPare Strings) allows the CPU to compare two strings, the source string being in the data segment and the destination string being in the extra segment. The strings may either be specified in bytes or in words; if DF = 0 the strings are compared in the forward direction, or in the reverse direction if DF = 1.

The CMPS instruction subtracts the destination byte or word (address by DI) from the source byte or word (address by SI); it sets the flags according to the

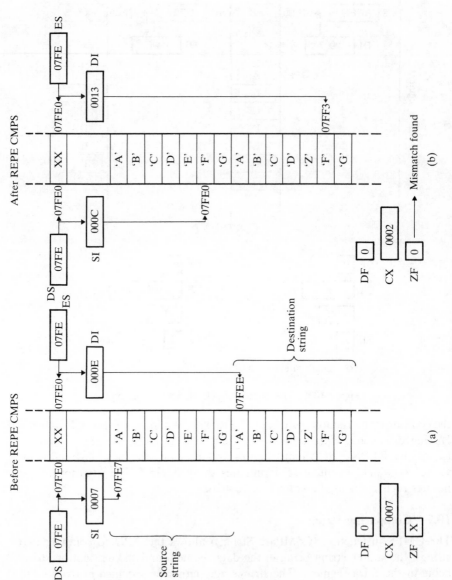

Figure 10.5 Using the REPE CMPS instruction to detect a mismatch between strings.

```
 1: ;****USE OF THE CMPS INSTRUCTION – LISTING 10.8****
 9: STRING    DB    'ABCDEFG'
10: STRING_2      DB      'ABCDZFG'
21:          LEA  SI,STRING          ;LOAD ADDRESS OF STRING
22:          LEA  DI,STRING_2        ;LOAD ADDRESS OF NEW STRING
23:          CLD                     ;FORWARD MOVE
24: ;
25:          REPE CMPS  STRING_2,STRING   ;COMPARE STRINGS
```

result, but discards the result. The CPMS instruction may be prefixed with REPE or REPZ.

An example of the use of the compare strings instruction REPE CMPS is illustrated in Listing 10.8. This is a modification of Listing 10.1, and contains the amended program lines.

The program compares, on a byte-by-byte basis, the destination string (STRING_2) with the source string (STRING). If the bytes compared are equal, the REPE instruction allows the CPU to compare the next pair of characters in the strings. Each COMPS instruction updates the SI and DI registers, and the REPE instruction decrements CX and checks the state of the ZF. If the bytes compared are equal, the ZF is set; if not, it is cleared. An escape is made from the REPE CMPS instruction either if all the characters are the same (the string length being stored in CX), or if two characters are found to be unequal. If two characters are unequal, the SI and DI registers indicate the character *after* the point where they differ.

The mechanics of the operation of the REPE CMPS instruction is shown in Fig. 10.5. Initially the SI register addresses the first character in STRING, and the DI register addresses the first character in STRING_2. The CMPS compares (subtracts) these characters from one another and, depending on the state of the ZF after this instruction, the REPE prefix either (if ZF = 1) allows the CPU to move to the next character in the string, or (if ZF = 0) escapes from the REPE CMPS instruction and executes the next instruction in sequence (which, in our case, terminates the program).

The sampling and comparing process continues until the SI register addresses the character 'E' in STRING and the DI register addresses 'Z' in STRING_2. The comparison process gives a non-zero result (ZF = 0), and the REPE prefix causes the CPU to leave the CMPS instruction, but not before the SI and DI registers have been incremented and the CX register decremented. Hence, when the mismatch is found, the SI and DI registers point to the character *after* the mismatch, i.e., both point to character 'F' in the two strings.

References for further study

1. *MCS-86 User's Manual*, Intel Corporation.
2. *MCS-86 Assembly Language Reference Manual*, Intel Corporation.
3. R. Rector and G. Alexy, *The 8086 Book: Including the 8088*, Osborne/ McGraw-Hill.
4. S. P. Morse, *The 8086/8088 Primer*, Hayden Book Company.
5. D. C. Willen and J. I. Krantz, *8088 Assembler Language Programming: The IBM P.C.*, Sams.
6. J. W. Coffron, *Programming the 8086/8088*, Sybex.
7. N. M. Morris, *Control Engineering*, 3rd Edition, McGraw-Hill.
8. N. M. Morris, *Logic Circuits*, 3rd Edition, McGraw-Hill.
9. N. M. Morris, *Microelectronic and Microprocessor-Based Systems*, Macmillan, London.

Appendix A
The 8088 instruction set

The information provided here has been extracted from *Intel Assembly Language Reference Manuals,* and is reprinted here with the permission of the Intel Corporation.

Key to Flag Codes

Code	Meaning
1	unconditionally set
0	unconditionally cleared
X	altered to reflect operation result
U	undefined (mask it out)
R	replaced from memory (e.g., SAHF)

AAA	AAA (no operands) ASCII adjust for addition	Flags	O D I T S Z A P C U U U X U X

Operands	Clocks	Transfers*	Bytes	Coding example
(no operands)	4	—	1	AAA

AAD	AAD (no operands) ASCII adjust for division	Flags	O D I T S Z A P C U X X U X U

Operands	Clocks	Transfers*	Bytes	Coding example
(no operands)	60	—	2	AAD

AAM	AAM (no operands) ASCII adjust for multiply	Flags	O D I T S Z A P C U X X U X U

Operands	Clocks	Transfers*	Bytes	Coding example
(no operands)	83	—	1	AAM

*For the 8086, add four clocks for each 16-bit transfer with an odd address. For the 8088, add four clocks for each 16-bit word transfer.
Mnemonics © Intel, 1978

AAS	AAS (no operands) ASCII adjust for subtraction			Flags	O D I T S Z A P C U U U X U X
Operands	Clocks	Transfers*	Bytes		Coding example
(no operands)	4	—	1		AAS

ADC	ADC destination, source Add with carry			Flags	O D I T S Z A P C X X X X X X
Operands	Clocks	Transfers*	Bytes		Coding example
register, register	3	—	2		ADC AX, SI
register, memory	9+EA	1	2–4		ADC DX, BETA [SI]
memory, register	16+EA	2	2–4		ADC ALPHA [BX] [SI], DI
register, immediate	4	—	3–4		ADC BX, 256
memory, immediate	17+EA	2	3–6		ADC GAMMA, 30H
accumulator, immediate	4	—	2–3		ADC AL, 5

ADD	ADD destination, source Addition			Flags	O D I T S Z A P C X X X X X X
Operands	Clocks	Transfers*	Bytes		Coding example
register, register	3	—	2		ADD CX, DX
register, memory	9+EA	1	2–4		ADD DI, [BX].ALPHA
memory, register	16+EA	2	2–4		ADD TEMP, CL
register, immediate	4	—	3–4		ADD CL, 2
memory, immediate	17+EA	2	3–6		ADD ALPHA, 2
accumulator, immediate	4	—	2–3		ADD AX, 200

AND	AND destination, source Logical and			Flags	O D I T S Z A P C 0 X X U X 0
Operands	Clocks	Transfers*	Bytes		Coding example
register, register	3	—	2		AND AL,BL
register, memory	9+EA	1	2–4		AND CX,FLAG_WORD
memory, register	16+EA	2	2–4		AND ASCII [DI],AL
register, immediate	4	—	3–4		AND CX,0F0H
memory, immediate	17+EA	2	3–6		AND BETA,01H
accumulator, immediate	4	—	2–3		AND AX, 01010000B

CALL	CALL target Call a procedure			Flags	O D I T S Z A P C
Operands	Clocks	Transfers*	Bytes		Coding examples
near-proc	19	1	3		CALL NEAR_PROC
far-proc	28	2	5		CALL FAR_PROC
memptr16	21+EA	2	2–4		CALL PROC_TABLE [SI]
regptr16	16	1	2		CALL AX
memptr32	37+EA	4	2–4		CALL [BX].TASK [SI]

CBW	CBW (no operands) Convert byte to word			Flags	O D I T S Z A P C
Operands	Clocks	Transfers*	Bytes		Coding example
(no operands)	2	—	1		CBW

*For the 8086, add four clocks for each 16-bit transfer with an odd address. For the 8088, add four clocks for each 16-bit word transfer.
Mnemonics © Intel, 1978

CLC	CLC (no operands) Clear carry flag			Flags	O D I T S Z A P C 0
Operands	Clocks	Transfers*	Bytes	Coding example	
(no operands)	2	—	1	CLC	

CLD	CLD (no operands) Clear direction flag			Flags	O D I T S Z A P C 0
Operands	Clocks	Transfers*	Bytes	Coding example	
(no operands)	2	—	1	CLD	

CLI	CLI (no operands) Clear interrupt flag			Flags	O D I T S Z A P C 0
Operands	Clocks	Transfers*	Bytes	Coding example	
(no operands)	2	—	1	CLI	

CMC	CMC (no operands) Complement carry flag			Flags	O D I T S Z A P C X
Operands	Clocks	Transfers*	Bytes	Coding example	
(no operands)	2	—	1	CMC	

CMP	CMP destination, source Compare destination to source			Flags	O D I T S Z A P C X X X X X X
Operands	Clocks	Transfers*	Bytes	Coding example	
register, register	3	—	2	CMP BX, CX	
register, memory	9+EA	1	2–4	CMP DH, ALPHA	
memory, register	9+EA	1	2–4	CMP [BP+2], SI	
register, immediate	4	—	3–4	CMP BL, 02H	
memory, immediate	10+EA	1	3–6	CMP [BX].RADAR [DI], 3420H	
accumulator, immediate	4	—	2–3	CMP AL, 00010000 B	

CMPS	CMPS dest-string,source-string Compare string			Flags	O D I T S Z A P C X X X X X X
Operands	Clocks	Transfers*	Bytes	Coding example	
dest-string, source-string	22	2	1	CMPS BUFF1, BUFF2	
(repeat) dest-string, source-string	9+22/rep	2/rep	1	REPE CMPS ID, KEY	

CWD	CWD (no operands) Convert word to doubleword			Flags	O D I T S Z A P C
Operands	Clocks	Transfers*	Bytes	Coding example	
(no operands)	5	—	1	CWD	

*For the 8086, add four clocks for each 16-bit transfer with an odd address. For the 8088, add four clocks for each 16-bit word transfer.
Mnemonics © Intel, 1978

DAA	DAA (no operands) Decimal adjust for addition			Flags	O D I T S Z A P C X X X X X X		
Operands	Clocks	Transfers*	Bytes	Coding example			
(no operands)	4	—	1	DAA			

DAS	DAS (no operands) Decimal adjust for subtraction			Flags	O D I T S Z A P C U X X X X X		
Operands	Clocks	Transfers*	Bytes	Coding example			
(no operands)	4	—	1	DAS			

DEC	DEC destination Decrement by 1			Flags	O D I T S Z A P C X X X X X		
Operands	Clocks	Transfers*	Bytes	Coding example			
reg16	2	—	1	DEC AX			
reg8	3	—	2	DEC AL			
memory	15+EA	2	2–4	DEC ARRAY [SI]			

DIV	DIV source Division, unsigned			Flags	O D I T S Z A P C U U U U U		
Operands	Clocks	Transfers*	Bytes	Coding example			
reg8	80–90	—	1	DIV CL			
reg16	144–162	—	2	DIV BX			
mem8	(86–96) +EA	1	2–4	DIV ALPHA			
mem16	(150–168) +EA	1	2–4	DIV TABLE [SI]			

ESC	ESC external-opcode,source Escape			Flags	O D I T S Z A P C		
Operands	Clocks	Transfers*	Bytes	Coding example			
immediate, memory	8+EA	1	2–4	ESC 6,ARRAY [SI]			
immediate, register	2	—	2	ESC 20,AL			

HLT	HLT (no operands) Halt			Flags	O D I T S Z A P C		
Operands	Clocks	Transfers*	Bytes	Coding example			
(no operands)	2	—	1	HLT			

IDIV	IDIV source Integer division			Flags	O D I T S Z A P C U U U U U		
Operands	Clocks	Transfers*	Bytes	Coding example			
reg8	101–112	—	2	IDIV BL			
reg16	165–184	—	2	IDIV CX			
mem8	(107–118) +EA	1	2–4	IDIV DIVISOR_BYTE [SI]			
mem16	(171–190) +EA	1	2–4	IDIV [BX]. DIVISOR_WORD			

*For the 8086, add four clocks for each 16-bit transfer with an odd address. For the 8088, add four clocks for each 16-bit word transfer.
Mnemonics © Intel, 1978

IMUL

| **IMUL** | IMUL source
Integer multiplication | | | | Flags | O D I T S Z A P C
X   U U U U X |

Operands	Clocks	Transfers*	Bytes	Coding example
reg8	80–98	—	2	IMUL CL
reg16	128–154	—	2	IMUL BX
mem8	(86–104) +EA	1	2–4	IMUL RATE_BYTE
mem16	(134–160) +EA	1	2–4	IMUL RATE_WORD [BP] [DI]

IN

| **IN** | IN accumulator,port
Input byte or word | | | | Flags | O D I T S Z A P C |

Operands	Clocks	Transfers*	Bytes	Coding example
accumulator, immed8	10	1	2	IN AL,0FFEAH
accumulator, DX	8	1	1	IN AX,DX

INC

| **INC** | INC destination
Increment by 1 | | | | Flags | O D I T S Z A P C
X   X X X X |

Operands	Clocks	Transfers*	Bytes	Coding example
reg16	2	—	1	INC CX
reg8	3	—	2	INC BL
memory	15+EA	2	2–4	INC ALPHA [DI] [BX]

INT

| **INT** | INT interrupt-type
Interrupt | | | | Flags | O D I T S Z A P C
0 0 |

Operands	Clocks	Transfers*	Bytes	Coding example
immed8 (type = 3)	52	5	1	INT 3
immed8 (type ≠ 3)	51	5	2	INT 67

INTR†

| **INTR†** | INTR (external maskable interrupt)
Interrupt if INTR and IF=1 | | | | Flags | O D I T S Z A P C
0 0 |

Operands	Clocks	Transfers*	Bytes	Coding example
(no operands)	61	7	N/A	N/A

INTO

| **INTO** | INTO (no operands)
Interrupt if overflow | | | | Flags | O D I T S Z A P C
0 0 |

Operands	Clocks	Transfers*	Bytes	Coding example
(no operands)	53 or 4	5	1	INTO

IRET

| **IRET** | IRET (no operands)
Interrupt Return | | | | Flags | O D I T S Z A P C
R R R R R R R R R |

Operands	Clocks	Transfers*	Bytes	Coding example
(no operands)	24	3	1	IRET

*For the 8086, add four clocks for each 16-bit transfer with an odd address. For the 8088, add four clocks for each 16-bit word transfer.
†INTR is not an instruction; it is included only for timing information.
Mnemonics © Intel, 1978

JA/JNBE

JA/JNBE short-label Jump if above/Jump if not below nor equal				Flags O D I T S Z A P C
Operands	Clocks	Transfers*	Bytes	Coding example
short-label	16 or 4	—	2	JA ABOVE

JAE/JNB

JAE/JNB short-label Jump if above or equal/Jump if not below				Flags O D I T S Z A P C
Operands	Clocks	Transfers*	Bytes	Coding example
short-label	16 or 4	—	2	JAE ABOVE_EQUAL

JB/JNAE

JB/JNAE short-label Jump if below/Jump if not above nor equal				Flags O D I T S Z A P C
Operands	Clocks	Transfers*	Bytes	Coding example
short-label	16 or 4	—	2	JB BELOW

JBE/JNA

JBE/JNA short-label Jump if below or equal/Jump if not above				Flags O D I T S Z A P C
Operands	Clocks	Transfers*	Bytes	Coding example
short-label	16 or 4	—	2	JNA NOT_ABOVE

JC

JC short-label Jump if carry				Flags O D I T S Z A P C
Operands	Clocks	Transfers*	Bytes	Coding example
short-label	16 or 4	—	2	JC CARRY_SET

JCXZ

JCXZ short-label Jump if CX is zero				Flags O D I T S Z A P C
Operands	Clocks	Transfers*	Bytes	Coding example
short-label	18 or 6	—	2	JCXZ COUNT_DONE

JE/JZ

JE/JZ short-label Jump if equal/Jump if zero				Flags O D I T S Z A P C
Operands	Clocks	Transfers*	Bytes	Coding example
short-label	16 or 4	—	2	JZ ZERO

JG/JNLE

JG/JNLE short-label Jump if greater/Jump if not less nor equal				Flags O D I T S Z A P C
Operands	Clocks	Transfers*	Bytes	Coding example
short-label	16 or 4	—	2	JG GREATER

*For the 8086, add four clocks for each 16-bit transfer with an odd address. For the 8088, add four clocks for each 16-bit word transfer.
Mnemonics © Intel, 1978

JGE/JNL	JGE/JNL short-label Jump if greater or equal/Jump if not less	Flags	O D I T S Z A P C
Operands	Clocks	Transfers*	Bytes	Coding example
short-label	16 or 4	—	2	JGE GREATER_EQUAL

JL/JNGE	JL/JNGE short-label Jump if less/Jump if not greater nor equal	Flags	O D I T S Z A P C
Operands	Clocks	Transfers*	Bytes	Coding example
short-label	16 or 4	—	2	JL LESS

JLE/JNG	JLE/JNG short-label Jump if less or equal/Jump if not greater	Flags	O D I T S Z A P C
Operands	Clocks	Transfers*	Bytes	Coding example
short-label	16 or 4	—	2	JNG NOT_GREATER

JMP	JMP target Jump	Flags	O D I T S Z A P C
Operands	Clocks	Transfers*	Bytes	Coding example
short-label	15	—	2	JMP SHORT
near-label	15	—	3	JMP WITHIN_SEGMENT
far-label	15	—	5	JMP FAR_LABEL
memptr16	18+EA	1	2–4	JMP [BX].TARGET
regptr16	11	—	2	JMP CX
memptr32	24+EA	2	2–4	JMP OTHER.SEG [SI]

JNC	JNC short-label Jump if not carry	Flags	O D I T S Z A P C
Operands	Clocks	Transfers*	Bytes	Coding example
short-label	16 or 4	—	2	JNC NOT_CARRY

JNE/JNZ	JNE/JNZ short-label Jump if not equal/Jump if not zero	Flags	O D I T S Z A P C
Operands	Clocks	Transfers*	Bytes	Coding example
short-label	16 or 4	—	2	JNE NOT_EQUAL

JNO	JNO short-label Jump if not overflow	Flags	O D I T S Z A P C
Operands	Clocks	Transfers*	Bytes	Coding example
short-label	16 or 4	—	2	JNO NO_OVERFLOW

*For the 8086, add four clocks for each 16-bit transfer with an odd address. For the 8088, add four clocks for each 16-bit word transfer.
Mnemonics © Intel, 1978

JNP/JPO

JNP/JPO short-label
Jump if not parity/Jump if parity odd

Flags O D I T S Z A P C

Operands	Clocks	Transfers*	Bytes	Coding example
short-label	16 or 4	—	2	JPO ODD_PARITY

JNS

JNS short-label
Jump if not sign

Flags O D I T S Z A P C

Operands	Clocks	Transfers*	Bytes	Coding example
short-label	16 or 4	—	2	JNS POSITIVE

JO

JO short-label
Jump if overflow

Flags O D I T S Z A P C

Operands	Clocks	Transfers*	Bytes	Coding example
short-label	16 or 4	—	2	JO SIGNED_OVRFLW

JP/JPE

JP/JPE short-label
Jump if parity/Jump if parity even

Flags O D I T S Z A P C

Operands	Clocks	Transfers*	Bytes	Coding example
short-label	16 or 4	—	2	JPE EVEN_PARITY

JS

JS short-label
Jump if sign

Flags O D I T S Z A P C

Operands	Clocks	Transfers*	Bytes	Coding example
short-label	16 or 4	—	2	JS NEGATIVE

LAHF

LAHF (no operands)
Load AH from flags

Flags O D I T S Z A P C

Operands	Clocks	Transfers*	Bytes	Coding example
(no operands)	4	—	1	LAHF

LDS

LDA destination,source
Load pointer using DS

Flags O D I T S Z A P C

Operands	Clocks	Transfers*	Bytes	Coding example
reg16,mem32	16+EA	2	2–4	LDS SI,DATA.SEG [DI]

LEA

LEA destination,source
Load effective address

Flags O D I T S Z A P C

Operands	Clocks	Transfers*	Bytes	Coding example
reg16,mem16	2+EA	—	2–4	LEA BX,[BP] [DI]

*For the 8086, add four clocks for each 16-bit transfer with an odd address. For the 8088, add four clocks for each 16-bit word transfer.
Mnemonics © Intel, 1978

LES	LES destination,source Load pointer using ES			Flags	O D I T S Z A P C
Operands		Clocks	Transfers*	Bytes	Coding example
reg16,mem32		16 + EA	2	2–4	LES DI,[BX].TEXT_BUFF

LOCK	LOCK (no operands) Lock bus			Flags	O D I T S Z A P C
Operands		Clocks	Transfers*	Bytes	Coding example
(no operands)		2	—	1	LOCK XCHG FLAG,AL

LODS	LODS source-string Load string			Flags	O D I T S Z A P C
Operands		Clocks	Transfers*	Bytes	Coding example
source-string (repeat) source-string		12 9 + 13/rep	1 1/rep	1 1	LODS CUSTOMER_NAME REP LODS NAME

LOOP	LOOP short-label Loop			Flags	O D I T S Z A P C
Operands		Clocks	Transfers*	Bytes	Coding example
short-label		17/5	—	2	LOOP AGAIN

LOOPE/LOOPZ	LOOPE/LOOPZ short-label Loop if equal/Loop if zero			Flags	O D I T S Z A P C
Operands		Clocks	Transfers*	Bytes	Coding example
short-label		18 or 6	—	2	LOOPE AGAIN

LOOPNE/LOOPNZ	LOOPNE/LOOPNZ short-label Loop if not equal/Loop if not zero			Flags	O D I T S Z A P C
Operands		Clocks	Transfers*	Bytes	Coding example
short-label		19 or 5	—	2	LOOPNE AGAIN

NMI†	NMI (external nonmaskable interrupt) Interrupt if NMI = 1			Flags	O D I T S Z A P C 0 0
Operands		Clocks	Transfers*	Bytes	Coding example
(no operands)		50	5	N/A	N/A

*For the 8086, add four clocks for each 16-bit transfer with an odd address. For the 8088, add four clocks for each 16-bit word transfer.
Mnemonics © Intel, 1978
†NM1 is not an instruction; it is included only for timing information

MOV	MOV destination,source Move			Flags	O D I T S Z A P C
Operands	Clocks	Transfers*	Bytes		Coding example
memory, accumulator	10	1	3		MOV ARRAY [SI], AL
accumulator, memory	10	1	3		MOV AX, TEMP_RESULT
register, register	2	—	2		MOV AX,CX
register, memory	8 + EA	1	2–4		MOV BP, STACK_TOP
memory, register	9 + EA	1	2–4		MOV COUNT [DI], CX
register, immediate	4	—	2–3		MOV CL, 2
memory, immediate	10 + EA	1	3–6		MOV MASK [BX], [SI], 2CH
seg-reg, reg16	2	—	2		MOV ES, CX
seg-reg, mem16	8 + EA	1	2–4		MOV DS, SEGMENT_BASE
reg16, seg-reg	2	—	2		MOV BP, SS
memory, seg-reg	9 + EA	1	2–4		MOV [BX].SEG_SAVE, CS

MOVS	MOVS dest-string,source-string Move string			Flags	O D I T S Z A P C
Operands	Clocks	Transfers*	Bytes		Coding example
dest-string,source-string	18	2	1		MOVS LINE, EDIT_DATA
(repeat) desi-string,source-string	9 + 17/rep	2/rep	1		REP MOVS SCREEN, BUFFER

MOVSB/MOVSW	MOVSB/MOVSW (no operands) Move string (byte/word)			Flags	O D I T S Z A P C
Operands	Clocks	Transfers*	Bytes		Coding example
(no operands)	18	2	1		MOVSB
(repeat) (no operands)	9 + 17/rep	2/rep	1		REP MOVSW

MUL	MUL source Multiplication, unsigned			Flags	O D I T S Z A P C X U U U U X
Operands	Clocks	Transfers*	Bytes		Coding example
reg8	70–77	—	2		MUL BL
reg16	118–133	—	2		MUL CX
mem8	(76–83) + EA	1	2–4		MUL MONTH [SI]
mem16	(124–139) + EA	1	2–4		MUL BAUD_RATE

NEG	NEG destination Negate			Flags	O D I T S Z A P C† X X X X X 1†
Operands	Clocks	Transfers*	Bytes		Coding example
register	3	—	2		NEG AL
memory	16 + EA	2	2–4		NEG MULTIPLIER

*For the 8086, add four clocks for each 16-bit transfer with an odd address. For the 8088, add four clocks for each 16-bit word transfer.
†0 if destination = 0
Mnemonics © Intel, 1978

NOP	NOP (no operands) No Operation			**Flags** O D I T S Z A P C
Operands	Clocks	Transfers*	Bytes	Coding example
(no operands)	3	—	1	NOP

NOT	NOT destination Logical not			**Flags** O D I T S Z A P C
Operands	Clocks	Transfers*	Bytes	Coding example
register	3	—	2	NOT AX
memory	16+EA	2	2–4	NOT CHARACTER

OR	OR destination,source Logical inclusive or			**Flags** O D I T S Z A P C 0 X X U X 0
Operands	Clocks	Transfers*	Bytes	Coding example
register, register	3	—	2	OR AL,BL
register, memory	9+EA	1	2–4	OR DX,PORT ID [DI]
memory, register	16+EA	2	2–4	OR FLAG_BYTE,CL
accumulator, immediate	4	—	2–3	OR AL,01101100B
register, immediate	4	—	3–4	OR CX,01H
memory, immediate	17+EA	2	3–6	OR [BX].CMD_WORD,0CFH

OUT	OUT port,accumulator Output byte or word			**Flags** O D I T S Z A P C
Operands	Clocks	Transfers*	Bytes	Coding example
immed8, accumulator	10	1	2	OUT 44, AX
DX, accumulator	8	1	1	OUT DX, AL

POP	POP destination Pop word off stack			**Flags** O D I T S Z A P C
Operands	Clocks	Transfers*	Bytes	Coding example
register	8	1	1	POP DX
seg-reg (CS illegal)	8	1	1	POP DS
memory	17+EA	2	2–4	POP PARAMETER

POPF	POPF (no operands) Pop flags off stack			**Flags** O D I T S Z A P C R R R R R R R R
Operands	Clocks	Transfers*	Bytes	Coding example
(no operands)	8	1	1	POPF

*For the 8086, add four clocks for each 16-bit transfer with an odd address. For the 8088, add four clocks for each 16-bit word transfer.
Mnemonics © Intel, 1978

PUSH

PUSH source				
Push word onto stack				**Flags** O D I T S Z A P C

Operands	Clocks	Transfers*	Bytes	Coding example
register	11	1	1	PUSH SI
seg-reg (CS legal)	10	1	1	PUSH ES
memory	16+EA	2	2–4	PUSH RETURN_CODE [SI]

PUSHF

PUSHF (no operands)				
Push flags onto stack				**Flags** O D I T S Z A P C

Operands	Clocks	Transfers*	Bytes	Coding example
(no operands)	10	1	1	PUSHF

RCL

RCL destination,count				
Rotate left through carry				**Flags** O D I T S Z A P C X X

Operands	Clocks	Transfers*	Bytes	Coding example
register, 1	2	—	2	RCL CX, 1
register, CL	8+4/bit	—	2	RCL AL, CL
memory, 1	15+EA	2	2–4	RCL ALPHA, 1
memory, CL	20+EA+ 4/bit	2	2–4	RCL [BP].PARM, CL

RCR

RCR designation,count				
Rotate right through carry				**Flags** O D I T S Z A P C X X

Operands	Clocks	Transfers*	Bytes	Coding example
register, 1	2	—	2	RCR BX,1
register, CL	8+4/bit	—	2	RCR BL, CL
memory, 1	15+EA	2	2–4	RCR [BX].STATUS, 1
memory, CL	20+EA+ 4/bit	2	2–4	RCR ARRAY [DI], CL

REP

REP (no operands)				
Repeat string operation				**Flags** O D I T S Z A P C

Operands	Clocks	Transfers*	Bytes	Coding example
(no operands)	2	—	1	REP MOVS DES, SRCE

REPE/REPZ

REPE/REPZ (no operands)				
Repeat string operation while equal/while zero				**Flags** O D I T S Z A P C

Operands	Clocks	Transfers*	Bytes	Coding example
(no operands)	2	—	1	REPE CMPS DATA, KEY

REPNE/REPNZ

REPNE/REPNZ (no operands)				
Repeat string operation while not equal/not zero				**Flags** O D I T S Z A P C

Operands	Clocks	Transfers*	Bytes	Coding example
(no operands)	2	—	1	REPNE SCAS INPUT_LINE

*For the 8086, add four clocks for each 16-bit transfer with an odd address. For the 8088, add four clocks for each 16-bit word transfer.
Mnemonics © Intel, 1978

RET

RET optional-pop-value Return from procedure			Flags	O D I T S Z A P C

Operands	Clocks	Transfers*	Bytes	Coding example
(intra-segment, no pop)	8	1	1	RET
(intra-segment, pop)	12	1	3	RET 4
(inter-segment, no pop)	18	2	1	RET
(inter-segment, pop)	17	2	3	RET 2

ROL

ROL destination,count Rotate left			Flags	O D I T S Z A P C X X

Operands	Clocks	Transfers*	Bytes	Coding example
register, 1	2	—	2	ROL BX, 1
register, CL	8+4/bit	—	2	ROL DI, CL
memory, 1	15+EA	2	2–4	ROL FLAG_BYTE [DI],1
memory, CL	20+EA+ 4/bit	2	2–4	ROL ALPHA, CL

ROR

ROR designation,count Rotate right			Flags	O D I T S Z A P C X X

Operands	Clocks	Transfers*	Bytes	Coding example
register, 1	2	—	2	ROR AL, 1
register, CL	8+4/bit	—	2	ROR BX, CL
memory, 1	15+EA	2	2–4	ROR PORT_STATUS, 1
memory, CL	20+EA+ 4/bit	2	2–4	ROR CMD_WORD, CL

SAHF

SAHF (no operands) Store AH into flags			Flags	O D I T S Z A P C R R R R R

Operands	Clocks	Transfers*	Bytes	Coding example
(no operands)	4	—	1	SAHF

SAL/SHL

SAL/SHL destination,count Shift arithmetic left/Shift logical left			Flags	O D I T S Z A P C X X

Operands	Clocks	Transfers*	Bytes	Coding example
register, 1	2	—	2	SAL AL,1
register, CL	8+4/bit	—	2	SHL DI, CL
memory, 1	15+EA	2	2–4	SHL [BX] OVERDRAW,1
memory, CL	20+EA+ 4/bit	2	2–4	SAL STORE COUNT,CL

SAR

SAR destination,source Shift arithmetic right			Flags	O D I T S Z A P C X X X U X X

Operands	Clocks	Transfers*	Bytes	Coding example
register, 1	2	—	2	SAR DX,1
register, CL	8+4/bit	—	2	SAR DI, CL
memory, 1	15+EA	2	2–4	SAR N_BLOCKS,1
memory, CL	20+EA+ 4/bit	2	2–4	SAR N_BLOCKS,CL

*For the 8086, add four clocks for each 16-bit transfer with an odd address. For the 8088, add four clocks for each 16-bit word transfer.
Mnemonics © Intel, 1978

SBB

SBB destination,source Subtract with borrow				Flags	O D I T S Z A P C X X X X X X

Operands	Clocks	Transfers*	Bytes	Coding example
register, register	3	—	2	SBB BX, CX
register, memory	9+EA	1	2–4	SBB DI, [BX].PAYMENT
memory, register	16+EA	2	2–4	SBB BALANCE, AX
accumulator, immediate	4	—	2–3	SBB AX, 2
register, immediate	4	—	3–4	SBB CL, 1
memory, immediate	17+EA	2	3–6	SBB COUNT [SI], 10

SCAS

SCAS dest-string Scan string				Flags	O D I T S Z A P C X X X X X X

Operands	Clocks	Transfers*	Bytes	Coding example
dest-string	15	1	1	SCAS INPUT_LINE
(repeat) dest-string	9+15/rep	1/rep	1	REPNE SCAS BUFFER

SEGMENT†

SEGMENT override prefix Override to specified segment				Flags	O D I T S Z A P C

Operands	Clocks	Transfers*	Bytes	Coding example
(no operands)	2	—	1	MOV SS:PARAMETER, AX

SHR

SHR destination,count Shift logical right				Flags	O D I T S Z A P C X X

Operands	Clocks	Transfers*	Bytes	Coding example
register, 1	2	—	2	SHR SI, 1
register, CL	8+4/bit	—	2	SHR SI, CL
memory, 1	15+EA	2	2–4	SHR ID_BYTE [SI] [BX], 1
memory, CL	20+EA+ 4/bit	2	2–4	SHR INPUT_WORD, CL

SINGLE STEP‡

SINGLE STEP (Trap flag interrupt) Interrupt if TF = 1				Flags	O D I T S Z A P C 0 0

Operands	Clocks	Transfers*	Bytes	Coding example
(no operands)	50	5	N/A	N/A

STC

STC (no operands) Set carry flag				Flags	O D I T S Z A P C 1

Operands	Clocks	Transfers*	Bytes	Coding example
(no operands)	2	—	1	STC

*For the 8086, add four clocks for each 16-bit transfer with an odd address. For the 8088, add four clocks for each 16-bit word transfer.
†ASM-86 incorporates the segment override prefix into the operand specification and not as a separate instruction. SEGMENT is included only for timing information.
‡SINGLE STEP is not an instruction, it is included only for timing information.
Mnemonics © Intel, 1978

STD	STD (no operands) Set direction flag			Flags	O D I T S Z A P C 1
Operands	Clocks	Transfers*	Bytes	Coding example	
(no operands)	2	—	1	STD	

STI	STI (no operands) Set interrupt enable flag			Flags	O D I T S Z A P C 1
Operands	Clocks	Transfers*	Bytes	Coding example	
(no operands)	2	—	1	STI	

STOS	STOS dest-string Store byte or word-string			Flags	O D I T S Z A P C
Operands	Clocks	Transfers*	Bytes	Coding example	
dest-string	11	1	1	STOS PRINT_LINE	
(repeat) dest-string	9 + 10/rep	1/rep	1	REP STOS DISPLAY	

SUB	SUB destination,source Subtraction			Flags	O D I T S Z A P C X X X X X X
Operands	Clocks	Transfers*	Bytes	Coding example	
register, register	3	—	2	SUB CX, BX	
register, memory	9 + EA	1	2–4	SUB DX, MATH_TOTAL [SI]	
memory, register	16 + EA	2	2–4	SUB [BP + 2], CL	
accumulator, immediate	4	—	2–3	SUB AL, 10	
register, immediate	4	—	3–4	SUB SI, 5280	
memory, immediate	17 + EA	2	3–6	SUB [BP].BALANCE, 1000	

TEST	TEST destination,source Test or non-destructive logical AND			Flags	O D I T S Z A P C 0 X X U X 0
Operands	Clocks	Transfers*	Bytes	Coding example	
register, register	3	—	2	TEST SI, DI	
register, memory	9 + EA	1	2–4	TEST SI, END_COUNT	
accumulator, immediate	4	—	2–3	TEST AL, 00100000B	
register, immediate	5	—	3–4	TEST BX, 0CC4H	
memory, immediate	11 + EA	—	3–6	TEST RETURN_CODE, 01H	

WAIT	WAIT (no operands) Wait while TEST pin not asserted			Flags	O D I T S Z A P C
Operands	Clocks	Transfers*	Bytes	Coding example	
(no operands)	3 + 5n	—	1	WAIT	

*For the 8086, add four clocks for each 16-bit transfer with an odd address. For the 8088, add four clocks for each 16-bit word transfer.
Mnemonics © Intel, 1978

XCHG	**XCHG** destination,source Exchange			**Flags** O D I T S Z A P C
Operands	Clocks	Transfers*	Bytes	Coding example
accumulator, reg16	5	—	1	XCHG AX, BX
memory, register	17+EA	2	2–4	XCHG SEMAPHORE, AX
register, register	4	—	2	XCHG AL, BL

XLAT	**XLAT** source-table Translate			**Flags** O D I T S Z A P C
Operands	Clocks	Transfers*	Bytes	Coding example
source-table	11	1	1	XLAT ASCII_TAB

XOR	**XOR** destination,source Logical exclusive or			**Flags** O D I T S Z A P C 0 X X U X 0
Operands	Clocks	Transfers*	Bytes	Coding example
register, register	3	—	2	XOR CX, BX
register, memory	9+EA	1	2–4	XOR CL, MASK_BYTE
memory, register	16+EA	2	2–4	XOR ALPHA [SI], DX
accumulator, immediate	4	—	2–3	XOR AL, 01000010B
register, immediate	4	—	3–4	XOR SI, 00C2H
memory, immediate	17+EA	2	3–6	XOR RETURN_CODE, 0D2H

*For the 8086, add four clocks for each 16-bit transfer with an odd address. For the 8088, add four clocks for each 16-bit word transfer.
Mnemonics © Intel, 1978

Appendix B
The ASCII code

HEX	MSD	0	1	2	3	4	5	6	7
LSD	BITS	000	001	010	011	100	101	110	111
0	0000	NUL	DLE	SPACE	0	@	P	—	p
1	0001	SOH	DC1	!	1	A	Q	a	q
2	0010	STX	DC2	"	2	B	R	b	r
3	0011	ETX	DC3	#	3	C	S	c	s
4	0100	EOT	DC4	$	4	D	T	d	t
5	0101	ENQ	NAK	%	5	E	U	e	u
6	0110	ACK	SYN	&	6	F	V	f	v
7	0111	BEL	ETB	'	7	G	W	g	w
8	1000	BS	CAN	(	8	H	X	h	x
9	1001	HT	EM	)	9	I	Y	i	y
A	1010	LF	SUB	*	:	J	Z	j	z
B	1011	VT	ESC	+	;	K	[	k	{
C	1100	FF	FS	,	<	L	\	l	--
D	1101	CR	GS	–	=	M	]	m	}
E	1110	SO	RS	.	>	N	∧	n	~
F	1111	SI	US	/	?	O	←	o	DEL

THE ASCII SYMBOLS

NUL – Null
SOH – Start of heading
STX – Start of text
EXT – End of text
EOT – End of transmission
ENQ – Enquiry
ACK – Acknowledge
BEL – Bell
BS – Backspace
HT – Horizontal tabulation
LF – Line feed
VT – Vertical tabulation
FF – Form feed
CR – Carriage return
SO – Shift out
SI – Shift in

DLE – Data link escape
DC – Device control
NAK – Negative acknowledge
SYN – Synchronous idle
ETB – End of transmission block
CAN – Cancel
EM – End of medium
SUB – Substitute
ESC – Escape
FS – File separator
GS – Group separator
RS – Record separator
US – Unit separator
SP – Space (Blank)
DEL – Delete

Index